D1194005

Woman's Doctor

A Year in the Life of an Obstetrician-Gynecologist

By Dr. WILLIAM J. SWEENEY III
with Barbara Lang Stern

William Morrow & Company, Inc.   New York   1973

To my mother and father, Esther and William Sweeney

W.J.S.

For Ernie

B.L.S.

Contents

Author to Reader

Many times when I am at a party a lady will ask, "How can you even look at a woman after what you do all day?" Or a man will jab me in the ribs and say, "Aren't you ashamed to take money for handling all that stuff?"

I have often wondered whether people really know what it's like to be an obstetrician and gynecologist. To be so chronically exhausted that you literally fall asleep in the middle of dinner. To be so conditioned to crises that you jump whenever a phone rings, even if the phone is part of a television program. Or to be the person who has to tell a woman she has a cancer.

On the other hand, do people understand the sheer joy of delivering a baby, or the pride and accomplishment you feel when you know your operation was well done and your patient will be healthy because of you? Do they know how great it is to look forward to going to work?

About two years ago, a patient of mine who is a writer suggested that we coauthor a book. I thought, "I don't know how I'll have the time, but I want to do it." And somehow since then this book has been written.

Woman's Doctor is first of all a true story covering approximately one year in my life as an obstetrician-gynecologist. In a separate section, I have tried to answer some of the medical questions women most frequently bring me. I have thought about patients who will soon be seeing an OB-GYN man and may not know what to ask, or may be afraid to bring up some particular problem. Will he laugh at them, be annoyed or ignore them? Perhaps they will find it easier to have some of their questions answered in a book. They may even be reassured to know others share their concerns. Certainly women deserve clear and candid information that will dispel some common misconceptions that often cause needless worry.

A story plus questions and answers. Not a conventional book, perhaps, but one that I hope will move, amuse and inform. Maybe *Woman's Doctor* will also explain why I and many other doctors feel we are among the most fortunate people in the world.

WILLIAM J. SWEENEY III, M.D.

Woman's Doctor

PART ONE

Days and Nights

1. Jean Simpson

My fingertips touched the telephone as I listened in the dark bedroom for a second ring. If you've ever been awakened suddenly from a deep sleep, you know the heart-pounding alarm that's followed by a few seconds' adjustment to reality. I wasn't positive I hadn't been dreaming. Sometimes I dream the phone is ringing and jerk awake to silence; other times I'm operating while I sleep and wake myself cutting, or holding out my hand for an instrument.

The second ring started and I grabbed the receiver. "Hello."

"Dr. Sweeney, this is your service. Mrs. Collins is on the line. She says it's not an emergency but she'd like to speak to you if possible."

I tried to place the name. Not one of my pregnant ladies. "What's the problem?"

"She didn't want to say. She just asked me to tell you it was Marsha Chamberlin Collins."

Marsha Chamberlin. She's been married less than a year

and I still thought of her by her maiden name. "Okay, I'm up now, give her this number."

My wife Fran turned in bed. "Nice timing," she said. "You haven't been asleep more than half an hour."

"My God, I thought it was the middle of the night."

I left the light off and waited, wondering what was wrong with Marsha. Most people are pretty considerate about calling their doctors at night—although we've been awakened more times than we'd like by someone phoning from a party: "Dr. Sweeney, we were just having an argument about some medical thing. . . ." I'm ready to murder that jerk. I don't like to be nasty, but occasionally I am if the call obviously could have waited. I had a woman phone a couple of weeks ago in the wee hours. "Dr. Sweeney," she said, "I have an itch."

"*Scratch it!*" I said and hung up, but by then I was awake, wide-eyed and fuming because I was so goddamned mad.

A minute later Marsha was on the line. "Dr. Sweeney, I'm so sorry to bother you. It's not even really a medical problem but I don't know what to do and I didn't know who else to ask—"

"Okay, take it easy. What's the matter?"

"Bob and I were at a party tonight and we came home and went to bed together—I mean, we made love together." Embarrassment replaced the worry in her voice. I half-expected what came next. "We were just lying here and I remembered I didn't take my pill this morning. I don't know if it will do any good for me to take one now or if there's anything else I can do."

"It won't hurt to take your pill, but I can't promise you'll be safe. Did you use a douche?"

"No, I thought it would just push everything up and make matters worse."

I couldn't help smiling. "It won't push anything up that hasn't already gone there, and it may wash out some of the semen. It's no contraceptive, but it's better than nothing. And Marsha, call me tomorrow; you should take some other precautions for the rest of the month."

"I will. And I'm so sorry I woke you."

"That's all right." I meant it. She was just a worried young girl. "I'll be asleep before you are," I said. I hung up, knowing I'd gotten off easy with that call. By the time my head hit the pillow again I had already dismissed it from my mind.

An obstetrician-gynecologist learns to go to sleep quickly and soundly because if he doesn't, he won't survive. I may have three or four calls during the night, but I don't count them; I just roll over. In the morning I might say, kind of surprised, "I slept all night."

"Well, you took four phone calls while you were sleeping," my wife will answer.

"Oh, yeah, but that's all right, I didn't get up." Then I may ask, "Did I say anything?" Because sometimes I forget what I said, although the information I gave was correct.

But if somebody calls in trouble or in labor, I'm wide-awake. It was 4:30 A.M. when the service rang again. Ed Simpson had called. His wife Jean was in strong labor. I sat up, swung my legs over the side of the bed and switched on the light. I took the Simpsons' number—there's always a pencil and paper alongside the bed when I go to sleep—and got Ed immediately. I spoke to him briefly, then to Jean. Her contractions were ten minutes apart. She had been doing her natural childbirth exercises and wasn't sure she should have awakened me yet. I told her I was glad she felt calm but I hadn't planned to sleep through this first baby of hers. "You've got plenty of time," I said, "but have Ed take you to the Admitting Office on Seventieth Street and I'll meet you upstairs."

The New York Hospital is a large complex of connected buildings, with The Lying-In, the obstetrical and gynecological unit, at the north end. I phoned to tell Admitting that Jean was on her way. It's nice for a woman to arrive and hear, "Oh yes, Mrs. Simpson, we've been expecting you."

I dressed quickly, automatically. A woman about to have her first baby is usually examined in the hospital by one of the resident physicians. He then calls to tell me how close she is to delivery. But contractions ten minutes apart mean labor is well under way, and I wanted to see how Jean was progressing.

Jean Simpson came to me five years ago for her gynecological checkup before getting married. She was twenty-two then, a pretty girl with long brown hair, large hazel eyes and a remarkable curiosity. After I'd examined her for the first time, she asked, "Dr. Sweeney, would you tell me what it actually looks like inside?"

That surprised me, and I suddenly thought that of the thousands of women I examine, very few ask what I'm seeing through the speculum. "The cervix looks like the tapered end of a cigar, head-on, and it projects into the vagina for a centimeter and a half—a little more than half an inch," I said. "In the middle, a small canal connects the vagina and the inside of the uterus, letting the sperm enter or the menstrual flow come out." She nodded, waiting. "A nonpregnant cervix and vagina are pink, like the inside of your mouth. A pregnant cervix has a purplish-bluish tint to it. We could use that coloration as a pregnancy test except the lights we work under usually take out the bluish color and we don't want to examine women in the daylight to make sure the cervix is blue."

Jean grinned and thanked me for the information. After that, she generally had one or two inquiries per session: What was I feeling when I examined her? Why did I take several samples for a Pap test? Why did I do a rectal examination each time? Good intelligent questions that I enjoyed answering, although occasionally I wondered at her interest in knowing exactly what I was doing and why. A couple of years later I got my answer when we had to hospitalize Jean. She had sharp pain in the left lower abdomen, nausea, vomiting and loss of appetite. Examining her in the office, I hadn't been able to determine what was the matter. Her uterus and ovaries felt normal; her abdomen wasn't distended, but she had pain in her side whether I pressed on it or not.

In the hospital we gave her fluids intravenously because she was weak and dehydrated from the vomiting. I called in an internist, and for two days we ran tests and took X-rays which ruled out a lot but didn't identify the problem. The third morning I told Jean I wanted to do a surgical examination. She picked up a typewritten permission form that already lay on her bed and read aloud: " 'Emergency abdominal exploratory.' The nurse brought it in a few minutes ago. It means you don't know what's the matter, doesn't it?"

"Sometimes we have to look and see."

I waited for questions but there was just a carefully controlled statement: "Dr. Sweeney, I'm quite frightened of hospitals. And of not knowing." Her hazel eyes were large, the iris sharply outlined with a green-gray ring, and tawny flecks near the pupils.

"I don't know any more than I've told you, Jean. I won't ever lie to you, but I won't make guesses."

She stared at me. "And I won't sign that permission," she said, rejection and distrust tightening her face.

No doctor likes to think a patient doesn't trust him. I felt a prick of temper, but at the same time compassion for this girl. She was frightened, understandably, and I was asking permission to perform any surgery deemed necessary while we were doing the exploratory. "Why don't you think it over, Jean? Nobody can make you sign anything. I can't even keep you here; you can go home today. But you're sick and you need help." There was no response.

In the corridor a nicely dressed woman introduced herself

as Mrs. Singleton, Jean's mother. I told her briefly how things stood. "I'm sure Jean will sign the permission," Mrs. Singleton said. "She just needs a little time to get used to the idea of an operation she doesn't understand." Mrs. Singleton walked a few steps with me. "Jean's only been in the hospital once before." I waited because she obviously wanted to tell me more. Then she explained that Jean had cut her hand when she was a little girl. Her parents had taken her to the hospital, where the doctors operated and saved her finger, but the tendon had been severed. Tendon grafts weren't perfected in those days, and when Jean came home, she couldn't straighten her finger. Mrs. Singleton demonstrated quickly, showing me her own right hand, palm up, all the fingers extended except the fourth which she bent up at a 90 degree angle from the middle joint. "When the stitches had healed," she continued, "they were afraid the tendon would shrink, so for the next six months I took Jean to the doctor's office every day and held her on my lap with her hand out so he could pull on her finger to stretch it." Jean's mother took a deep breath. "She used to scream the whole time we were there, from fright as much as pain. I kept explaining the treatment was helping her. But how could I make a three-year-old understand why she had to keep going back like that?" The question had no answer, but the account explained some things about Jean.

I saw two other patients on the floor and was heading for the stairs when a nurse caught up with me. "Mrs. Simpson was asking if you were still around."

I returned to Jean's room.

"Dr. Sweeney, I'm sorry about before," she said as soon as I entered. She held out the permission form, signed. "Sometimes I just act dumb."

"I don't think you act dumb. I'd say you were one of my prettiest, smartest patients." I got a wavery smile. I told her the nurse would pick up the form and we would schedule her operation for the next morning. "Is there anything you'd like to ask me?"

She shook her head. "No more questions," she said very softly. Too softly, I thought.

"Are you sure?"

She studied me. Suddenly she leaned forward and indicated the permission form. "What on earth is a 'laparotomy'?" she demanded with some of her usual spirit.

I grinned, actually relieved. "Any abdominal operation."

"Pretty fancy language," she commented, and I think we both felt better.

What Jean had was quite unusual and happily not very serious: a small blood vessel had broken in the wall of the tiny sac on her ovary from which an egg had been ovulated. The bleeding into her abdominal cavity was causing the pain. It was a simple procedure to suture the blood vessel in the ovary and stop the bleeding.

When Jean's office visits resumed, her questions were about pregnancy. She and Ed were planning to have children after they had saved a little more money. Ed was an associate editor with a news magazine, and Jean taught remedial reading. "I love children," she said. "If you listen to them, they tell you the most fascinating things."

Jean became pregnant a year and a half later, but two months into her pregnancy, she miscarried. It's awful to lose a baby you really want, and Jean was crying miserably when she called me from her home. "I can't believe it's happening," she sobbed, "but there are cramps and blood and some clots—"

"Jean," I cut in, "are you saving the stuff you pass?"

"I got a bowl when I felt the clots," she said.

"Okay, now listen: save everything. Put it in a jar and pour some booze or any kind of alcohol on it so it won't dry out. Just don't use water because that'll destroy it."

We want women to bring us all the expelled matter so

we can examine it. The worst thing is to have somebody call and say, "It's all over."

"What's all over?"

"I just had a miscarriage."

"What did you do with it?"

"I flushed it."

Well, that doesn't help anybody very much. If the woman brings us the stuff she has passed, we send it to the Pathology Lab and sometimes they can tell us why the miscarriage took place. Maybe something was wrong with the conceptus, which is what we call the fetus (unborn baby) plus the placenta. Or perhaps a problem in the lining of the uterus made it impossible for the pregnancy to continue. Besides, a woman doesn't know the difference between clots and tissue. Maybe she's just passed a clot or two and I can reassure her that she's still pregnant. Certainly I wouldn't want to take her to the hospital to complete the miscarriage and end up aborting the baby.

I asked Jean, "Is Ed home yet?"

"No, the magazine is closing its issue tonight and he's got a story to finish."

"I think you ought to call him."

"No."

"Jean, I think he should be at home with you."

"Why should he have to see this whole mess?" she asked bitterly. "There's nothing he can do here anyway. And this story he's worked on is important to him."

I couldn't talk her into anything. She understood what was happening and was going to handle it herself.

The next afternoon Jean brought me a small jar filled with dark-brown blood clots and tissue. "What are you doing here?" I said. "I told you to have Ed bring this over. You should be home in bed."

"I'm going right home from here—in a taxi." So what could I say?

We examined Jean two days later, got the report from the lab and confirmed that she had indeed miscarried, but for no cause they could determine. That was the hardest thing for her to accept. All women who miscarry want a reason. She sat in my office asking, "Why did it happen?" Then she started blaming herself because she and Ed had given a party a couple of nights before and she had gone marketing and carried home some packages. "But I didn't think they were that heavy," she said. "Maybe I didn't get enough rest," she blurted. "Sometimes I couldn't fall asleep and I read—" It was a desperate confession of everything she could think of that might have caused the miscarriage.

"Okay, Jean, now cut it out," I said. Then I told her there probably had been something wrong with the fetus and nature had gotten rid of it. It could well be true, and most women can accept the idea that it is better to lose the baby than to have a defective child months later.

"Wouldn't the laboratory have found out if something was wrong with the fetus?"

"Not necessarily."

"But you don't really know why I lost my baby," she said. Her look reminded me of the first time I saw her in the hospital.

"Jean, the absolute truth is that between 10 and 20 percent of all pregnancies end in miscarriage, and usually we don't know the reason."

She was silent for a long moment and then said quietly, "Thank you for telling me the truth, Dr. Sweeney. I guess sometimes things happen where no one is to blame." And she didn't discuss the miscarriage again.

Now, fourteen months later, Jean was at the end of a successful pregnancy. But she still had to complete her labor and deliver her baby.

When I got to the hospital at 5 A.M., the Simpsons were already upstairs in one of the labor rooms which are lined up along one side of an L-shaped wing on the eighth floor. At the far end of the corridor are four delivery rooms, which are like small operating rooms. Jean was in a hospital gown, looking huge like all ladies when they are due. Dr. Max Richards, the resident, was about to examine her.

"You got here so fast!" she said when I walked in. "They really rushed me up. I think they were afraid I'd give birth in the lobby."

"It's happened," I told her. "How do you feel?"

"Nervous," she admitted. "And kind of ridiculous. The pains were regular but now I haven't had any for twelve minutes. You don't think I could have gotten you up for another false alarm?"

Jean had come into the office with cramps the week before, but it had turned out to be false labor. She had apologized for bothering me and been annoyed with herself. "They told us all about this in natural childbirth class," she'd said firmly.

"Well, I'm a doctor and even I didn't know it was false labor until I examined you," I'd answered just as firmly. Now I told her there was very little doubt that she was in labor: her contractions had been regular since midnight and getting closer every hour.

Dr. Richards, the resident, and Miss Kovacs, the labor nurse, stayed in the room, but we sent Ed out while I examined Jean. I put my sterile gloved forefinger into her vagina and moved it around the opening of the cervix. You can feel how big the opening into your nostril or your ear is, and that's what it feels like when the cervix is a little dilated.

"It's no false alarm this time," I told Jean. "You're about three centimeters dilated, and everything looks just fine."

During labor, powerful uterine muscle contractions make the cervix, or mouth of the uterus, open or dilate. Since the average baby's head measures 9.5 centimeters, the cervix has to open to about 10 centimeters before the baby can be born. Some hospitals talk in terms of "fingers," and you'll hear a doctor say a patient is so many fingers dilated. But my finger, which is 1½ centimeters wide, may not be the same width as another doctor's, so I think that's an inaccurate way to give the measurement.

Ed came back into the room, and I put on a special stethoscope called a fetoscope. It's attached to a metal band that fits around my head like a miner's head lamp, leaving my hands free. By leaning down and placing the fetoscope on Jean's abdomen, I could hear and count the baby's heart rate. It was normal, beating 140 times a minute.

After Miss Kovacs took Jean's blood pressure, I told the Simpsons there would be several more hours of labor. Jean nodded knowingly, and I thought, "She must have been the star student in her natural childbirth class." Right then, she had a contraction that obviously hurt, but she did her panting exercise and when it was over, she looked pleased. "I'm starting again, and it's really like they said it would be, no worse than menstrual cramps!" She paused. "Are they going to shave me now?"

"Not now, and not at all," I answered.

"But in natural childbirth class they told us we'd have to be shaved."

"Well, in this hospital when you're my patient, you won't be."

I could see Jean comparing these conflicting bits of information. It's always been thought, at least since the development of modern techniques in preparing people for surgery, that any surgical area has to be shaved. Pregnant women are generally shaved in the perineum, or area of skin between the vaginal opening and the anus, where we normally make an incision called an episiotomy. This incision enables the lady to deliver without tearing. However, women are also shaved up over the entire mons, or pubic area. Well, the hair has to grow back and it itches and it sticks and it's ungodly. And if we're going to be operating on the vaginal outlet, why shave them up on the abdomen in the first place? The answer is, it's like everything else in medicine: if Lister did it, we do it. But some years ago I decided to take a random sample of women and skip shaving half of them to evaluate whether or not we got into more trouble. Lo and behold, we had no problems with those we didn't shave: no increase of infection, nothing. So then a few of us started to really examine this perineum we'd been looking at for twenty years and we found that there *is no hair* in the midline just outside the vaginal opening. Not even in the most hairy woman.

I told Jean and Ed about an argument I once had with a well-known doctor who claimed I had set obstetrics back twenty years because I didn't shave the patient. He was standing there talking to me with a moustache. I asked him, "If you were going to have your tonsils out tomorrow, would you want your moustache shaved off?" Which is exactly the same thing.

"Anyway, now they're changing," I said. "Some of them are doing half-shaves—just shaving the lower part. Called a poodle cut, I guess." Jean, Ed and Dr. Richards laughed, which made me feel pretty good because I'm a frustrated actor and I like to carry on like this.

Then I told Jean they'd probably give her an enema, and she grimaced but she understood that we usually do this because it's a little cleaner—a little more aesthetic. Otherwise, under the pressure of birth, the baby's head comes out along with the woman's feces.

By then it was a quarter to six in the morning and I went up to the locker room to shower and shave and get into a scrub suit. I've got razors everywhere—home, hospital, office

—so that I can shave whenever I have time. And I've got clothes hanging all over, or sometimes I wouldn't get my shirt changed from Monday to Thursday. By 6:15 A.M. I was hungry, but the hospital cafeteria didn't open until seven, so I got some coffee in the Solarium, a little room we have on the operating floor. I was regretting the sleep I had missed —obstetricians are chronically tired—but I couldn't have fallen back asleep anyway. I would have lain there wondering if this one was going to be all right.

In obstetrics we're always worrying about somebody. I wake up in the middle of the night thinking about a patient because that pregnant woman is sitting on dynamite for nine months. She's different from the gynecological patient who comes in with a problem. Either I handle that or I don't; I operate or I don't; in any case, the constant pressure is not there. But so many things can happen to a pregnant lady. Every time the phone rings, I jump a foot. What is it this time? And it's always something. Maybe it's just a pregnant woman calling to say she's nauseated, and I think, "Oh my God, did she vomit *again?*" But imagine how awful it must be to be vomiting all the time. Or it's an infertility patient who finally got pregnant and then calls because she suddenly started to bleed. Is she going to lose this baby? Then there's the final event—the delivery—tremendous pressure all the time. One minute everything's fine, the next minute the baby's dead. We're constantly alert, monitoring the fetal heart and trying to make sure that all is well. So obstetrics is a tough business.

But it's fun. It's a happy specialty. The patients are happy people to work with. And at the age of fifty I still get a bang out of delivering a baby. It's just a gorgeous, glorious thing. And honest to God, the greatest worry these ladies have is about their child, and this is what makes women beautiful. I deliver a woman who's been hurting like hell for six or twelve hours. She's got a big gash down there that I made and it's bleeding like the devil; there's blood all over the sheets and everything else, and this woman who has been lying there hurting—every single time, she says, "How's the baby?" Not one of them has ever said to me, "How am I?" I'm sure as lousy men we would be worrying about ourselves, but they're not.

2. Don't Drop the Baby

The racket in the hall sent all of us charging out of the Solarium to see what was going on. A screaming woman was strapped on a stretcher rapidly being wheeled around the corner by a couple of nurse's aides. An urgent page was sounding but the two doctors being called, plus a couple of nurses, were already running past the stretcher toward the delivery rooms. I followed in case I could help but there was already a full team present. The woman they had brought up was a Puerto Rican lady who had come in ready to deliver. When she wasn't screaming, she was yelling in Spanish, having reverted under the pain and stress of labor to her native tongue. It took both aides to get her onto the delivery table and shackle her hands while the anesthesiologist gave her some gas to relieve the pain. I hate the word *shackle*—it sounds terrible—but of course it's not done to be mean. If something hurts, you have a natural tendency to put your hands there, and since the vaginal area is supposed to be sterile, we have to strap some women's hands to the table to keep them out of the way. I watched for another minute, and when it was obvious that everything was under control, I went back down the corridor to the Simpsons.

The noise had stopped but Ed was standing in the doorway still staring toward the delivery room. Jean was sitting bolt upright in bed, arms braced behind her to support her weight. "My God, what's happening?" she asked.

"Just a woman having a baby. She almost didn't get here in time."

"But the screaming—it sounded as though she was being murdered," Jean said nervously.

"I guess it does sound bloodcurdling if you're not used to it," I reassured her, "but a lot of women scream, although most of them hardly remember it afterward."

Jean sank back on her elbows but she still looked disturbed.

"How do you feel?" I asked.

"Okay," she said. "I had the enema. It wasn't too bad."

"Nothing else by mouth from now on," I reminded her.

Ed had come back into the room. "What about the lollypops, Dr. Sweeney?" He indicated a bunch of cellophane-wrapped candies on the table, where there was also some talcum powder and a stopwatch. Lollypops are part of the natural childbirth routine. The sugar gives the woman who's laboring a little energy. Also, she has something to lick when her mouth gets dry. She's been taught to pant through the mouth when she has a contraction so she won't tense her muscles. The contraction is less painful that way. After all, only at a certain point is she trying to bear down to expel the baby. Most of the long hours are spent waiting out the contractions while the cervix dilates and the baby moves down into position.

"The lollypops are okay but you may not need them." I turned to Jean, who was still distracted, watching the door.

"I'm going to start an infusion now. We'll put it in the back of your hand so you can move around."

"An infusion," Jean said, her attention suddenly riveted on me. "I thought with natural childbirth I wouldn't need anything like that."

"I'd rather you had it," I replied, thinking that one thing wrong with obstetrics is it's really a surgical specialty but it's not approached as one. Nobody in his right mind would start an operation without an infusion running, yet babies are delivered without them every day. "We're only giving you glucose and water. You're not going to get fed or have anything to drink for hours, so it's valuable just to supply some energy and liquid. But it's also a precaution. Suppose something goes wrong during labor and we suddenly need to do a Caesarean section? If we've got an infusion going, we can switch to blood or anything else you need without losing precious time."

"I guess that makes sense," Jean agreed. She had a contraction just then, and Ed grabbed the stopwatch. She lay back, panting and watching him until it was finished and he announced, "Thirty seconds. You did beautifully, sweetheart."

She smiled faintly. "It's not the greatest feeling in the world," she murmured. Then as the pain left her completely, she took a breath and added more strongly, "But it's not bad."

The nurse came in with an infusion setup and brought it to the side of the bed. "Are you right-handed?" Miss Kovacs asked so I could insert the needle where it would inconvenience Jean the least.

"Does it have to be in my hand?" Jean asked quickly. It was the first reference I'd heard her make to her childhood injury.

"No, we can put it in your arm if you'd prefer," I said. I inserted the needle in the back of her left forearm, pushed the little plastic catheter into the vein and removed the needle. I was just taping the catheter in place when the lusty squalling of a newborn baby sounded clearly in the hall. We looked at each other and grinned at the healthy announcement of new life. It had been less than ten minutes since the shrieking mother had been rushed to the delivery room.

"Do you have many close calls like that?" Jean asked, wide-eyed.

"We have them a lot closer," I told her. "We've had women give birth in the lobby or the elevators—I've even delivered people in cabs. You know, the lady doesn't quite make it, and the cab comes roaring up to the emergency entrance, horn blowing, with the woman in the back seat. Many times we've run out and had to cut off her pants because the baby's head was right there. She's screaming and the cab driver is yelling, 'Get her out, get her the hell out!' because he doesn't want the cab all messed up. We try to move her into the hospital, but if it's too late, there she is in front of God and everybody, having her baby."

Ed and Jean glanced at each other and back at me.

"I had one husband who came roaring across the Triborough Bridge with his wife in the back seat screaming because she was hurting and about to give birth. He went through the toll booth without paying, he was so eager to get to the hospital. The toll attendants heard the screaming and the cops started chasing him because they thought he was beating or killing or kidnapping this woman—and besides, he hadn't paid the toll. So he came speeding down to the hospital with the cops in pursuit, sirens blaring, his wife shrieking. We went tearing out to his car and there was his wife on her way to having the baby. The cops finally caught on."

Then I told them about one pregnant woman who never

made it to the hospital. She had called me just before midnight. In labor, she thought. I told her to go to the hospital and have the night staff check her, and I'd meet her there if it was time. I alerted the hospital that she was on her way and to let me know if she was going to deliver soon. Then I rolled over and went back to sleep.

The next morning I hadn't heard from the hospital and when I went in for rounds this woman had not arrived. I had just started office hours when I got a frantic phone call from the husband: he had decided his wife wasn't really in labor and since it was the middle of the night and he was tired, he'd kept her home. Now, frantic phone call: "The baby's coming right this minute! What do I do?" He had called the cops, who were there, but these particular policemen had never delivered a baby before and everyone was terrified. So I stopped office hours, left a patient on the examining table and started telling the husband on the phone how to deliver a baby.

"Get a towel and tell me what's happening," I said to the husband.

"She's lying in bed and I can see the top of the baby's head!"

"Okay, try to get your wife turned crosswise in bed so her buttocks are at the side of the mattress. Move two chairs next to the bed so she can put her feet on them. That will put the delivery area right on the edge of the bed so we can work."

When the husband returned to the phone I asked, "Now what's happening?" I could hear the woman yelling in the background.

"The head's starting to come out!"

"Take your left hand and put it on top of the baby's head," I told him. "Don't hold it back, just steady it, barehanded. I hope you've washed your hands."

Yes, he'd done that when he went to get the towel. And thank God the phone was next to the bed. But please tell him what to do.

So I repeated, "You've got your left hand on top of the baby's head just to steady it. Put the towel over your right hand. The baby's going to be face down. As its head starts to come out, put your right hand back by your wife's rectum. With your fingers, push up *gently* on the baby's forehead as it comes out. Then try to get your fingers underneath the baby's chin."

And I could hear the screaming in the background, "Oh, it's coming, it's coming, oh my God!" Then the phone went crashing to the floor and I waited until one of the cops got on and said, "Tell me what to tell him."

"The baby's coming out face down?" I checked. Most babies do, but occasionally they'll come out sunny side up.

The cop said, "Yeah, yeah, that's right. Face down."

"Now he's keeping his left hand on top of the baby's scalp or head and with his right hand he's trying to get hold of the chin. Once he gets it, he can control the head and bring it out by just flexing his fingers. Tell him to flex his right fingers and bring that baby's head out *slowly*."

I heard him repeating this to the father and then he yelled into the phone, "It's out, the head is out!"

"Okay, take it easy. All you've got is the head. Tell the father to step back for a second. Nothing's going to happen. Just wait a bit and probably you'll notice the head is turning. It'll do that automatically."

I heard these instructions go to the father and we waited. In most cases, the head will turn automatically one way or the other. If it doesn't, then we turn it so that the shoulders will rotate into a position where they can come out. But *we* know which side the back is on so we know which way to turn the head without breaking the kid's neck. The father didn't know where the back was. I sat there sweating and hoping this baby was going to turn by itself. You see, no woman in the world is built big enough for a full-term baby to come out with the shoulders straight ahead. She's got two pelvic bones; to pass through these the baby has to turn and come under them sideways.

Finally I heard in the distance, "Oh my God, it's turning." And now the woman was really screaming, not just because she was afraid but because it hurt.

"Okay," I said, "now take the baby's head in both hands and gently, slowly pull the head down toward the floor."

The policeman was repeating what I was saying like a fast echo.

"You'll see the top shoulder start to come out, and once it does, then start to lift the baby slowly until the other shoulder comes out. And do this very gently, because if she suddenly pushes at that point, that's when she's going to tear."

The cop repeated what I'd told him and then he asked, "Tear what? What's going to tear?"

"Never mind," I told him. "Just do what I'm saying." Actually it's the baby's posterior shoulder that hooks up in there and tears the perineum, but they didn't have to know the medical stuff to get this baby out. I wasn't sure how much of what I'd said they'd understood to begin with, but I was in the office and all I could do was wait. And I could hear the screaming in the background, "Oh, it's coming, it's *coming. . . .*"

Then there was a crash and the cop said, "Jesus Christ, the phone cord just pulled the lamp over." And I heard him telling the other cop, "Fix the lamp, for Christ's sake, don't just stand there, pick up the goddamned lamp." He said to me, "What do we do now? It's half out, for God's sake."

"Don't worry about the baby's breathing or crying. Just pull gently and the body is going to start coming out. Then you'll see which side the back is on, and take that hand and slip it alongside the back. Finally when those legs come out, grab them so you don't drop the baby."

"The doc says don't drop the baby!" I heard him yell at the father.

"Hello," I said.

"What?"

"Will you please try to act calm and tell him everything I say." Then I repeated what I'd said before and added, "As the feet come out, grab them both in one hand so you can hold the baby up and keep your left hand on the head. That's all you've got to do for a second. Just hold it and see whether it's a boy or girl. Then it'll probably cry all by itself. If it doesn't, just rub its back or pat it on the feet."

The cop was repeating exactly what I'd said, and I was praying this would be a good delivery. Ten out of fifteen deliveries are normal anyway; we're just insurance policies. Then, a minute after the woman had stopped shrieking, I suddenly heard the baby screaming and crying.

"It's born!" the policeman said. "Can you hear it?"

"Yeah, I can hear it. What have you got?"

"What do you mean?"

"Is it a boy or a girl?"

"I think it's a boy."

"What do you mean, you *think*? Go look!"

"It's a boy," he said a minute later. "And doc, this is my first."

That made me laugh, and this poor cop must have thought I was a little crazy, but I was just expressing my relief. Actually, the police are usually tremendous in this situation. They deliver lots of babies, and they're pretty good obstetricians, most of them. Only this time there were two policemen who had never done it before.

The husband got on the phone: "Should I cut the cord?"

His voice was high with tension and excitement. "What should I cut the cord with?"

"Don't cut the cord," I told him. "Just take it easy and listen to me. Now you can wait without doing anything until the placenta or afterbirth comes out. Your wife will have some contractions and it will come out by itself. Then everything will be attached: baby, umbilical cord and placenta. And you can just put the baby and everything together in a bassinet and take it to whatever hospital is closest to you."

I think if I had been in his place I would have let the hospital finish the rest. But these people were all worried about "getting the baby separated," so I said, "Okay, take two shoelaces and boil them up. And throw a pair of scissors in the boiling water for a while. They won't be sterile but at least they'll be clean. Then take the shoelaces and tie the cord tightly in two spots, about two and three inches from the baby's stomach, and cut in between." While they were doing this, the woman started delivering the placenta. She hadn't torn and she wasn't bleeding, and I told them to get her and the baby and the placenta—save the placenta for a doctor to inspect to make sure it was all out—to the nearest hospital.

Which I hope they did; but I never heard from those people again. My secretary couldn't believe that. We sent them their last bill for office visits and didn't get paid. We sent it again and it came back returned. We tried to phone and they had moved. So finally I said, "Forget it." I don't think we ever really got across to that husband that he had had no right to evaluate whether or not his wife was in labor, and that he was a horse's ass for deciding she wasn't.

After I finished the story, I told Jean and Ed I was going to eat breakfast and make rounds, but I wouldn't leave the hospital. Then I said, "Jean, I know you and Ed are planning to have natural childbirth, but there's no reason for you to be a martyr. If you're hurting badly, tell Dr. Richards. You're not going to lose any face if you take a little Demerol."

"That's okay, Dr. Sweeney. The pains aren't that bad." She paused. "I just want my baby to be all right."

3. Rounds

At 7 A.M. the hospital cafeteria in the basement of the main building was filling up with people coming on first shift, which starts at eight. The operating rooms open at eight, too, so there were lots of nurses and maybe ten doctors getting breakfast. And visitors or relatives who had been in the hospital during the night. I could have taken Ed Simpson with me, but I didn't want to be too intimate with him while Jean was in labor. I think it's better for everyone concerned if I maintain a professional aloofness.

You don't have to know anyone in a hospital cafeteria to pick out the obstetricians. At one table you see a few doctors heatedly discussing something while they pick at their food. And then you see another group sit down and eat without saying a word. Only when they've finished will they lean back and talk a little. They're the obstetricians. The obstetrician has had so many meals interrupted that he eats while he can. When I'm at home, my family is only halfway through the meal by the time I've finished. I can't help it.

That morning I had breakfast with Ben Abrams, an obstetrician I've known for years. After we finished eating, we talked for a while about the conference of the American College of Obstetricians and Gynecologists we had just attended in the beginning of May. I had given a couple of papers, with slides and stuff, and Ben was kidding me about going on the stage when suddenly he was paged. "Here we go," he said and swallowed the last of his coffee and left.

It was just past 7:30 A.M., and before going back to Lying-In to check on Jean, I went up to the eighteenth floor in the main building to see Margaret Benning, an old patient of mine. She had come to my office for a regular checkup the week before, and when I felt the lump in her breast, I ordered a mammogram, or breast X-ray, and then signed her in right away. Dr. Reis, a general surgeon, operated on her, because in my hospital, gynecological surgeons don't do breast surgery. I spoke to him afterward: they had done a frozen section or immediate slide analysis while she was on the operating table yesterday afternoon. It was cancer, so they went ahead and did the radical, removing the entire breast and glands under the arm as well. Technically, a mastectomy is a "superficial" procedure in the sense that they're not going into any cavity to do it. What is a breast but a lump of fat with glands in it, sitting on top of the chest wall? As far as the woman is concerned, though, a radical mastectomy is certainly a big operation.

Mrs. Benning was sitting up in bed with her right arm in a sling. "Dr. Sweeney, what did they do to me?" she asked.

"What do you mean, what did they do to you?" I couldn't believe she hadn't been told.

"Did they take off my breast?"

"Yes, they did."

And that was the end of that. She didn't say, "Was it cancer?" She knew. She turned her head into the pillow. There was no shrieking or crying, but I couldn't predict how she'd react later on.

"Would you like me to stay for a while, Margaret?" I asked. She just shook her head without looking at me again, so I left.

It was her surgeon's responsibility to tell her. Maybe he had and she'd just been so groggy she didn't remember. Or maybe her family had asked him not to tell her right away. I was sure there was some explanation because Dr. Reis is a kind person, not the cold sort of knife wielder some surgeons are. I walked back to my own building hoping they'd gotten all the cancer and that everything would be all right.

At Lying-In, I saw Jean, made sure everything was going normally and then started rounds as I usually do, at eight o'clock, on the eighth floor, which is our operating as well as delivery floor. I always check the operating schedule, take a quick look in the delivery rooms just to see what's happening and then start walking down. I like to make rounds twice a day: once in the morning and once at night. If you've ever been a patient in a hospital, you realize how longingly you look forward to those visits from your doctor. But it's not always possible. If I have an eight o'clock operation that runs six hours, I may see each patient only once that day.

There's an art to making rounds: you can spend forever with somebody, or be in and out so fast the patient unfortunately doesn't get her questions answered. I tell my women to have a list of questions ready so they won't forget anything, and that way we can accomplish all we have to in the time available to me.

Lucy Carter had about forty questions waiting for me last night, and by this morning she had thought up several more. I'd delivered her baby girl five days before, and she was getting ready to leave the hospital. First of all she wanted to know when she could go out.

"You're going out to get home, aren't you?" I said. "So when you get there you can go out. Just don't do more than you feel up to."

She nodded, checked that question off, and asked, "When can I take a bath?"

"When the bleeding stops," I told her. That kind of gets the obstetrician off the hook. One patient will have lochia, or a bloody discharge, for one week, and the next woman will have it for two or three weeks. This way, she'll wait to bathe until the lining from the uterus has been sloughed. The uterus has to get back down to normal size, and the site where the placenta was attached has to heal over.

Then she wanted to know when she could have intercourse.

Now, a lot of doctors tell their patients not to have intercourse until they come back for their examination in four to six weeks. But I think if you tell people they can't have intercourse for six weeks before delivery and six weeks after, you're crazy if you believe they're going to obey you. I tell my women I don't care if they have intercourse right up until they come into the hospital. And I told Lucy that now she should wait until the bleeding stopped completely.

On any given day, I may have from three to ten patients in the hospital, depending on how many deliveries and operations I've done. This morning I stopped at the nurses' station on our private GYN floor and pulled out two charts from the rack. I checked for any notes that had been entered overnight. Mrs. O'Connell, the head floor nurse, was watching me. "What are you looking at the charts for?" she asked, smiling. "Just ask Judge Herman and she'll tell you what's new."

So I went around the corner to see Judge Herman, who is a lawyer and a really sharp little old lady. She sits erect when she talks, and shakes her head slightly like old people do, but she's smart. She's got gray hair pulled tightly back in a bun, and steely gray eyes that she fixes on you. If you try to look away when you're talking to her, she shifts around until she catches your eye again.

I don't think she actually practices law anymore, but she still manages her family's estate, and she's also a trustee for one of the fine New England women's colleges. She has a private duty nurse all the time because she doesn't want to be alone, and the nurse had already cranked up the bed. Judge Herman was sitting upright waiting for me.

"Good morning, Judge Herman. How's everything today?"

"You're right on time this morning, Dr. Sweeney. Didn't you have to 'do' someone today?" Her eyes were drilling into mine.

"No, I just came to visit. You don't really need me anyway."

She nodded, but she was still on her own train of thought. "There are times, Dr. Sweeney, when you really take me down," she said. "You don't operate, you 'do.' Last week you asked me, 'When am I doing you?' Isn't that an awful thing to say? And yesterday you told me you had done Mrs. Ingram down the hall. Well, you'd better spend some time with her this morning; she's worried she won't be able to urinate on her own."

Judge Herman knew everything that was happening on the floor, and she'd looked everything up. When she first came to me two years ago, I'm sure she went to the medical records: she knew almost as much about my life as I did. And since then, she's sent me dozens of patients. She's even said to me, "I sit and diagnose on the phone, you know. I told Fannie Resnik, 'Fannie, I think you have a cyst and you better go see Dr. Sweeney.'" And when Mrs. Resnik came in, she did have a cyst.

"Judge Herman," I said, "when are you going to medical school? We need you in the profession."

"Don't soft-soap me, young man. I'm on to you. I know what you do. You come up here and spread your charm for five minutes, and incidentally you slip in a barium enema!"

So how can you not love this old lady? But she's driving

that private duty nurse almost insane because she talks and talks.

"Did you have breakfast?" she asked me. "I have some *schnecken* my daughter brought yesterday. They're as small as a crab apple and twenty-five cents apiece to boot, but worth every penny. Loaded with honey, pecans and raisins. You should eat lots of honey. Best way in the world to get energy."

"I just had breakfast, but thank you."

"Then take some maple syrup home. I've got blueberry flavor today."

Her family is from New Hampshire and owns a company that manufactures maple syrup. You just never leave her room without something.

I had operated on Judge Herman to repair her vagina because when she'd had a previous hysterectomy, the doctor didn't attach the top of the vagina very well, so it fell out, and there it was, hanging there.

She's the one who said to me, "I suppose it looks like a windsock! To a pilot, anyway."

And it did. But don't ask me how she knew I flew planes in the war.

4. Screw Mrs. Whatshername

By 8:45 I was back with the Simpsons, and I didn't like the way Jean looked. First of all, she had been laboring since midnight and she had visibly aged. Even a layman can see this in a woman who's been in labor for hours. She's exhausted, drawn. It isn't called labor for nothing. But besides that, Jean looked as though she had been crying. And Ed didn't seem too happy, either.

"How are you doing?" I asked.

She smiled faintly. "All right." But she sounded drained. I took her pulse and listened to the baby's heart.

"Dr. Orsini was just in," Ed said. "Dr. Richards went off at eight. Dr. Orsini told us Jean is seven centimeters dilated." So she still had about an hour until her cervix opened to 10 centimeters. Then it would be another hour of harder labor during which she would be bearing down to push the baby headlong into the opened birth canal.

"Did you get any breakfast, Ed?" I asked.

"No."

"Why don't you go on out and get something. I'll stay with Jean for a while."

"I don't want to leave her, Dr. Sweeney. I've got to time the contractions and—"

"Wait outside, Ed, I want to examine Jean."

Actually that was just an excuse to give me a chance to find out what was going on. It didn't take long. She had a contraction and began panting through the mouth, but suddenly she stopped the exercise, curled over on her side and started sobbing. "I can't do it. I just can't do it. Oh my God, it hurts."

She was crying hard and holding her lower abdomen. I sat on the bed and she gripped my hands until it was over.

"For God's sake, Jean, why didn't you ask Dr. Orsini for some Demerol?"

"We wanted natural childbirth," she sobbed. "You said the pain might be like this, but *they* said if we did everything, it would just be like menstrual cramps." Her hazel eyes looked stricken behind the tears.

"I'll be right back." I picked up her chart from the end of the bed and went into the hall. Ed started into the room. "Wait out here for a few minutes," I said. He looked puzzled. "Just stay out." I went down the hall and told the nurse to get me 100 milligrams of Demerol and handed her Jean's chart with the order written. Demerol is a narcotic and it can't be ordered verbally.

When I returned to the room, Jean had stopped crying but she was still curled on her side. Miss O'Brien, the nurse who had replaced Miss Kovacs on the 8 A.M. shift, came in with the syringe and showed it to me. I said to Jean, "We're giving you an injection of Demerol. It will work within a few minutes, honey."

She nodded silently.

The nurse gave Jean the injection in her buttock and left.

After a minute Jean said, "Ed doesn't know how it feels."

"Neither do I, really, but let's try to tell him."

I called Ed in and told him we'd given Jean the Demerol.

"Ed, I'm so sorry," she whispered apologetically, "I just couldn't do it."

"Now listen, let's try to understand something," I said. "Some women have easier labors than others. Jean's not going through with natural childbirth because there's no reason on God's earth for her to suffer like that. It's archaic. Labor contractions are like nothing else in the world."

Ed had been nodding, watching Jean. Suddenly he looked vastly relieved. "I'm glad, Dr. Sweeney," he said. Then to Jean, "Oh sweetheart, I'm really glad. It looked awful."

Jean faced us. "I guess I have a low pain threshold or something," she said. "Even panting away like a lap dog, it hurt so much. I'm sorry."

"Jean, I'm going to turn you over and spank you, baby and all, if you start feeling guilty," I said. "The only pain probably close to that of labor contractions is trying to pass a kidney stone—and what have you got when you pass a kidney stone? At least at the end of this, you've got a baby to show."

Jean suffered through another contraction. Then the Demerol started working, and after the next spasm she said, "It makes such a difference. The pain is still there, but it's kind of distant." She looked at me uncertainly. "Do a lot of women think they're going to have natural childbirth and then give up?"

I nodded. "It happens all the time. As far as I'm concerned, one of the main problems of natural childbirth is that couples go to classes and get all prepared, but they're not told what the pain might really be like. I've had people come in to labor with playing cards or magazines or martinis, all set for a picnic because Mrs. Whatshername who ran the class said it wasn't going to hurt. The husband is there with powder so he can rub his wife's tummy, and he's got a stop-watch and he's timing every contraction—cheerleader, that's what he is—and everything's fine for a while."

Ed grinned sheepishly and Jean giggled a little. "Then what happens?" Ed asked.

"The wife goes through early labor and she's glowing: 'It's just like Mrs. Whatshername said it would be and we're going to have our baby together—' and *bam!* she goes into real labor. Suddenly it's excruciating and she shatters. Mrs. Whatshername who taught the course lied to her, and my God, most times this woman has nobody to turn to. First of all, she didn't get the rapport with her obstetrician that she needed. She got it with the woman who was teaching her how to breathe. Her husband, poor guy, is still saying, 'It's forty-five seconds, dear, breathe out . . .' and she says, 'Shut the hell up, you son-of-a-bitch, you got me into this.' And with that he's gone." Jean reached for Ed's hand. "So you two have done just fine."

The poor lady who really goes to pieces has to be sedated. There's nothing else we can do with her. She climbs the walls, she screams, shouts obscenities in our ear, and it isn't really her fault. She didn't purposely let herself be betrayed. I tell all my patients when they go to class, "Look, this thing hurts. Don't be conned into believing it doesn't." But a lot of them don't believe me.

"I've met women who had natural childbirth," Jean said.

"People have different pain tolerances," I replied. "But we don't give you a little star in the middle of your forehead for going through this without any analgesic or pain-killing drug. There's nothing to prove. I've had women tell me, 'I can't take anything because I'll fail with Mrs. Whatshername. I'm supposed to give her a written report.' Well, *screw* Mrs. Whatshername. At that point, take it."

Jean laughed out loud. I thought, I'll never understand what's so wonderful and modern about natural childbirth.

What the hell, if it's going to be really natural, the lady ought to deliver the baby and then eat the placenta. I mean, that's what animals do.

"Dr. Sweeney," Ed asked, "will I still be able to be in the delivery room with Jean?"

"Why not? Just because she's had an injection? That doesn't change anything. It's your baby. But I don't want you sitting there with your face in the way so I can't cut the episiotomy."

"I'll stay out of the way," he promised.

"Okay. And remember what I told you at the office: once we're in there, I'm interested in a mother and a baby. If you faint and fall flat on your face, we're too busy to bother with you. And if something comes up and I tell you to leave, out you go."

"Yes, sir," Ed responded. "I remember everything you said." I knew he was thinking about what I had told both of them: that not all births and not all babies are normal. You have to consider that possibility and be ready to take the bitter with the sweet.

I've had husbands in the delivery room for the birth of a baby that wasn't normal. One I remember in particular was a pillar of strength. Without him, I don't see how we'd ever have gotten through. His wife was awake. She had taken some drug in Germany and I think this was probably a thalidomide baby—an infant whose normal development was distorted by the tranquilizer his mother had taken during early pregnancy. It was born without arms and legs. The father of that baby picked it up and showed it to the mother right after it was born. "Here, look at it," he said. I guess that sounds cruel, but it wasn't. The love these two people had for each other was fantastic. I don't think there's anyplace you see more love than the delivery room. The wife cried, but right then they planned what they were going to do. I told them the baby probably would not survive, and it didn't, but they were talking about having another baby even while they were both crying and hanging onto each other. I delivered their next child, a healthy, sweet little girl.

I think without question we do more for marriages by letting the husband be there than by keeping him out. People come to New York City from miles around because so many of the outlying hospitals still won't let husbands in the delivery room. Of course it's not a good idea for everyone, but you can tell whether the husband wants to go through with it, and you know by the wife's eyes whether she really wants him there. In Russia today husbands aren't allowed in the hospital before or even after the baby is born. Until the mother goes home, nobody can visit her. I think that's just barbaric. Yet even in this country there are still places where the husband says good-bye to his wife at the hospital entrance and she's whisked upstairs to labor alone.

I always feel labor is like the greatest drama in the world —like somebody must be standing in the background beating a drum slowly and then faster and faster as the excitement builds and the climax is coming. *Nine* months we got ready for this, and finally we're here and this woman must think, "I'm center stage." In England the delivery room is called a theater. The birth itself is a big drama. There's a large white light shining down on the woman. The doctor is in there with his mask and gloves; the nurses are waiting on him, and he's a big ham, anyway. Most of us are. Time after time we're thrilled when we deliver a baby, and it must be the most joyous and profound moment in a woman's life.

5. Jean Simpson—Delivery

I had left the Simpsons shortly after nine to call my office: my secretary would be in by then. I made sure the service had told her to cancel morning visits, and I got a bunch of messages that were waiting for me. By 9:45 A.M. I had returned a dozen phone calls and I went back to see Jean.

She was having contractions every three minutes and feeling a lot of pain even through the haze Demerol creates. My examination showed the cervix was 8 centimeters dilated. I told her that instead of more Demerol, I was going to give her what's called a paracervical block.

This is an anesthesia I like a lot. Most of the severe pain in childbirth comes from the slowly dilating cervix, with the baby and the water pressing down against it. The paracervical block is injected on both sides of the cervix, deadening the nerves in the immediate area and actually aiding dilatation. The mother stays awake and the baby isn't born groggy, so this is a beautiful little anesthesia when properly used.

The nurse brought in a tray with the long sterile paracervical needle, syringe and local anesthetic agent. I had Jean lie on her back with her thighs apart while I directed the needle into position on each side of the cervix and injected the anesthesia.

A minute later Jean had a good contraction—nearly sixty seconds long. Her uterus under my hand was hard. The uterus is really a large muscle, and when it contracts, it feels like an athlete's biceps.

Ed was back in the room when Jean looked at me in amazement. "It didn't hurt," she exclaimed. "I could feel the contraction but there was no real pain."

I phoned my office one more time and then returned to stay with Jean.

About forty minutes later, she was fully dilated—10 centimeters or 4 inches. Now when her contractions came she was taking a breath and bearing down against her stomach, like a person straining with a bowel movement, in an effort to help the uterine muscles force the baby, head first, through the open cervix. This second stage of labor usually lasts about an hour. Jean was working hard, her contractions coming every two minutes, and not saying much to Ed or me. After a while she became anxious about when she would be going to the delivery room. Partly to reassure her and partly to help pass the time, I described how an obstetrician views the delivery of a primipara, or primip, as we call a woman having her first baby.

"We usually wait to take you to the delivery room until we can see a little bit of the baby's head showing at the vagina. You'll hear people on the delivery floor ask, 'How much caput do you have?' *Caput* means head. And they'll say, 'I've got twenty-five cents' worth,' or 'fifty cents' worth.' When we've got fifty cents' worth of caput, which means an area of visible head the size of a half dollar, we know we'd better take you to delivery."

Actually, I can easily understand a lady's getting nervous lying there with the baby's head in her vagina. But we're watching her closely and we have a pretty good idea of when she's ready to deliver. Now some women are going to fool us: one minute they've got caput the size of a dime and then boom—out it comes. However, you play percentages in everything you do, and most times we're safe with fifty cents' worth. The woman having her second or third child is the tough one to predict. That baby will come faster, so usually we take her down before caput, when her cervix is about 8 centimeters dilated.

The labor nurse checked with us more frequently now to see how things were progressing. Shortly before I expected we'd have caput, I asked Miss O'Brien to stay with Jean and told Ed to come with me. I wanted to get caps and masks and show him how to put his shoe covers on before he came into the delivery room.

When we came back the nurse motioned me aside. "Dr. Sweeney, the last time I took the fetal heart, it was one hundred twenty-five."

"Check it after the next contraction," I said. A normal fetal or baby's heart is 140. A fetal heart of 125 isn't dangerous, and it may only signify a transient distress—from pressure on the cord, for example—which causes the rate to drop during each contraction. But during labor, if anything changes from the norm, we all get a wary feeling.

The nurse listened after the next contraction and I stood at her side reading her entry in the chart: 11:15 A.M.—fetal heart 115.

Well, as long as the fetal heart is over 100, that's still not real fetal distress as far as I'm concerned, but now I was watching Jean like a hawk. That heartbeat could go right back up to 130 or 140 and everything would be fine. Or it could drop.

Jean was lying there looking quite comfortable between contractions, and Ed was showing her the shoe covers I'd given him.

"Get a blood pressure and pulse," I told the nurse.

The notations she made in the chart were normal. Blood pressure was 110/70 and pulse was 80.

Motioning Ed back, I examined Jean vaginally. The membranes were bulging into the vagina in front of the baby's head.

"Jean, I'm going to rupture your membranes now," I said. "It won't hurt. There are no nerves there, and it will speed things up a little."

Actually, the main reason I was doing this was to check the amniotic fluid, or water surrounding the baby, for meconium stains. Meconium is the brownish-green fecal material inside the fetus. In a breech birth, where the baby delivers buttocks first, it's usual for the pressure to force out the meconium. But if you start getting fecal matter coming from a baby in normal position, the sphincter muscles encircling the anus have started to relax and the baby's obviously in real distress.

I took an Allis clamp, which is a sharp, serrated instrument, and ruptured the sac. Some of the amniotic fluid came out over Jean's vulva and onto the white bedsheet. It was nice and clear.

I had a stethoscope on Jean's abdomen, waiting as she finished another contraction. The baby's heart rate had dropped to 104 and that was close enough.

"Give her some oxygen," I told the nurse.

The nurse grabbed the portable oxygen tank in the corner next to the labor cot, pulled out the mask and opened the valve. "We're going to give you some oxygen, Jean," I said. "I don't want you to fight it, just breathe normally."

I put the mask down over her face and her hands came up, trying to get rid of the mask so she could talk. The nurse grabbed her hands and I said, "Jean, listen to me. This is just oxygen. We're having a little trouble with the baby's heartbeat and the more oxygen you breathe, the better it is for the baby." She stopped fighting but her eyes were wide open with panic. How do you reassure a mother at that point? "We're trying to increase the baby's oxygenation and the pure oxygen you take will reach him through the placenta." I wondered if doctors would soon prove whether or not this oxygen is of any real value. "Now just breathe normally," I told her. I looked at the nurse: "Hit the buzzer."

The nurse went over to the wall fast and pulled the switch that sets off the emergency buzzer on the floor. When that buzzer rings, everybody comes running because no one knows what's going on, and when you're in trouble in a good hospital, everybody works.

A minute later the room was filled with people. I let the anesthesiologist take over the mask and told him, "The fetal heart is around one hundred. Get her into delivery." I turned toward Ed. "I don't know what we've got here. You can come in with us or not, or you can come in and leave, but we won't have time for you after this." Then I said to Dr. Orsini, "Let's go."

The resident and I ran down the hall. A scrub nurse, still in her gown, from one of the operating rooms was following us. She went right into the delivery room. I tied up the mask that had been hanging around my neck.

"She's deliverable," I told Dr. Orsini while we scrubbed at the sink in the alcove adjoining the delivery room. "The caput is through the cervix but it's going to be a midforceps delivery. I'd like to get it down a little lower if we have time."

An intern stepped in from the delivery room. "Doctor, the heart is ninety-six."

We stopped scrubbing and went in, water running off our elbows. Ed was in the room, and the anesthesiologist was at

Jean's head giving oxygen. The fundus (uterus) nurse, who stays with the woman throughout delivery, had the stethoscope on Jean's abdomen. Jean's legs were up in the stirrups and another nurse was prepping her, the disinfectant running down into the metal wash basin that's at the end of the delivery table. The amniotic fluid and blood go in there, or everything would be all over the floor.

"Okay, Jean, I'm right here," I said, identifying myself behind the mask. I was drying as fast as I could and getting into my sterile gear.

As soon as she heard me, Jean reached for the oxygen mask covering her nose and mouth so she could talk.

"Grab her hands," I said.

The intern held her wrists and she started to shake and twist her head frantically.

"Jean, listen to me. You're going to be all right. We just have to get the baby out a little sooner than we thought." She stopped twisting her head and stared at me, frightened to death. "We don't have to strap your hands down if you'll keep them by your sides, do you understand? You can't move them around or you'll get in our way."

She nodded and the intern slowly let go of her wrists. The nurse was taking Jean's blood pressure while the anesthesiologist gave her oxygen and watched the infusion. Dr. Orsini was holding the forceps.

I put my right forefinger inside Jean's vagina, touching the top of the baby's head. "When I tell you, honey, just push down as hard as you can and we'll have the baby where it'll be easy to get to him."

Theoretically you can put the forceps on as soon as the cervix is fully dilated. But I waited. The lower the baby, the easier the delivery. If this baby's head hadn't been well down into the pelvis, I would have done an emergency Caesarean rather than a difficult midforceps delivery.

Jean's next contraction came and I said, "Push now, Jean. *Push* as hard as you can."

She drew a breath and pushed. The baby's head moved slightly.

After the contraction, the fundus nurse said, "The fetal heart is ninety, doctor."

"Okay, let's get this baby out of there."

I took the forceps from Dr. Orsini. Forceps are like two big salad spoons which you cross, except they're much heavier, made of metal, and the blades have an oval hole in the center. I put the left spoon of the forceps up in the vagina with my left hand and then the right spoon with my right, feeling the spoons or blades as they lay over the sides of the baby's head, a little forward of the ears along the jaw. The baby has certain suture lines and openings in its head so the skull can contract and come through the relatively small delivery passage. The forceps have to be placed so the pressure is distributed over a large area or the skull might be injured.

In an elective forceps procedure, the point is to mimic labor: I pull, then let loose for a little bit, then pull some more. But in a forceps delivery for fetal distress, there's no time to imitate contractions. We can lose that baby. I locked the handles, sat down and pulled. A midforceps delivery is a pretty tough pull, like a drawer that's stuck. I could feel Jean's baby moving down through the vagina.

"Give her a local for the episiotomy," I told Dr. Orsini.

He injected Novocaine directly into the perineum. The paracervical block we'd done earlier affects only the nerves around the cervix, not those down between the vagina and anus where we were going to cut the episiotomy.

"Should I cut it?" Dr. Orsini asked, handing the syringe to the scrub nurse and picking up surgical scissors.

"Not yet," I said. "Wait until the head is crowning." I

kept pulling, wanting to get the head down as far as possible before cutting the episiotomy, because that's a very bloody area and one of the things that reduces the bleeding is the pressure of the baby's head.

"Okay, *cut it*," I said, keeping traction on the forceps. Dr. Orsini went in under the forceps with the scissors. He cut the perineum and up into the vagina, and blood spilled onto the green drapes covering the table and ran down toward the bucket between my feet.

The baby's head was halfway out of the vagina now. I took the forceps off because at that point I could deliver it better manually. I slid the fingers of my right hand under its chin and lifted up and out as hard as I dared. Jean had a contraction then. I heard Dr. Orsini tell her to push down, and suddenly the baby's head was out, followed by some of the fluid that could now get past its neck. I could feel the neck was clear, no umbilical cord wrapped around it. I turned the baby, working as quickly and gently as possible. The right or top shoulder came out first. Then I lifted and eased out the left one and the rest of the narrower, wet body followed without difficulty. "It's a boy," I said automatically, but I didn't like the looks of this just-born infant. Healthy babies are not pink, they're blue when they first emerge. The blood hasn't been as oxygenated in the uterus as it will be when the baby starts to breathe. After all, *in utero,* the infant is kept warm and does not use its lungs, so the lower level of oxygen passing through the placenta is enough to maintain the vital organs. But this baby was pallid, almost white, because his heart had been pumping blood at a reduced rate. And he was too limp. Even before a baby starts breathing, it's got a certain amount of muscle tone. If you pick up the leg, it doesn't just flop down again. The baby may even move its fingers. But this infant wasn't well. I put him in my lap and quickly sucked the mucus out of his nose and mouth with a little bulb syringe so he couldn't aspirate it. Then I clamped the cord as fast as I could to get him free of his mother. I didn't think he was going to start breathing on his own and I wasn't going to waste time just rubbing his back or feet. We had to get oxygenated blood going to that kid's brain quickly so there wouldn't be brain damage. I didn't even care whether he breathed, frankly: as long as his heart was beating, I could breathe for him to get the blood oxygenated.

"Watch Mrs. Simpson," I told Dr. Orsini.

I carried the motionless baby a few fast steps to a table along the wall. A nurse was ready with a baby laryngoscope. I put the tiny instrument in his mouth back against the larynx. With the light on it, I could see the trachea, or windpipe, that connects the larynx and the two bronchial passages into the lungs. Swiftly I put a tube down into the trachea. The nurse hooked it to an anesthetic bag attached to an oxygen machine, and I squeezed the black rubber balloon in my hand. The baby's narrow chest immediately rose as the collapsed, unused lungs inflated under the pressure of the oxygen being forced in.

We practice and practice this procedure. On dead babies. If we ever have a dead baby, we round up everybody in sight to drill in this technique so that when the time comes, we can be sure we'll put that tube in the trachea, not the esophagus. We have only about a minute, and it's not going to help that baby's brain if we pump up its stomach.

The machine we use has a meter on it so we can't pump too hard. I was listening to the baby's heart and lungs to make sure the oxygen was getting through. Squeezing the bag steadily, I waited to hear if his lungs were going to start functioning. And I had an awful, sickening feeling in the pit of my stomach.

Anybody who has done obstetrics has lost a baby that just

never breathed. Sometimes the autopsy shows a congenital defect of the lungs or nervous system. If the fetal heart dropped long before birth, we know the brain is already damaged. I'll choose not to work on that infant too hard, rather than give the mother a mentally injured child. The baby with extreme brain damage probably will never pick up spontaneous respiration. We could breathe for somebody for twenty years, I guess, but the question is whether that person is really alive. People say we shouldn't play God, but we have to. When I'm working on an infant, it's my decision whether or not to stop. I won't say we don't work on certain babies, but it's not with the enthusiasm and persistence we feel if everything has gone well and suddenly we've just got an infant that doesn't breathe for a few minutes. We work like *mad* on that one: there's not necessarily anything wrong with it. A baby who's had mild fetal distress can pick up spontaneous breathing and be just as healthy as the infant who was delivered without any complication.

Suddenly I heard Jean's expectant voice. "Can I see my baby?"

The silence in answer to her question caused her to cry out sharply, "My baby!"

"I've got him, honey," I said.

Anguish pierced her voice as she realized something was terribly wrong. "What's the matter?"

Ed answered steadily, "Dr. Sweeney's taking care of our baby, sweetheart."

"What do you mean, taking care of him?" A note of hysteria shattered her words. "What does that *mean*?"

"We're giving him some oxygen, Jean," I said.

"Mrs. Simpson, lie back. Please." It was Dr. Orsini. Then Ed's voice covered his: "You'll hurt yourself, sweetheart. You've got to listen to Dr. Orsini."

Someone came to the table and said, "I'm Dr. Rogan from

Pediatrics." So the emergency call had gone over to them.

"There are no obvious congenital defects and the heart rate is pretty good," I told him while he snapped on sterile gloves. He took the sterile stethoscope out of my hands and put it on the baby's chest. "Around one twenty," he confirmed.

"There was mild distress but nothing that would . . ." My voice trailed off as I studied the baby. He had begun to pink up a little from the oxygen being forced into his lungs. "I'm going to take out the tube and give him a chance," I decided.

We pulled the tube up and waited. I stared down at Jean's little boy, willing him to take that first breath. Twenty seconds and nothing happened except the pinkish color paled. We didn't have to say anything; we just put the tube back down and I asked Dr. Rogan, "Will you pump for a minute?"

I went back to Jean. As much as I may want to stay with the baby, the pediatrician is certainly as well qualified as I am to take care of the infant. My primary responsibility is the mother. A lot can happen to this woman who has just delivered: she can hemorrhage, she still has to deliver the placenta, and the episiotomy has to be sewn up.

Jean stared at me as I came to the table. "Please tell me how our baby is."

I can't lie to a mother at this point. Her baby wasn't breathing. "He's not very good right now, Jean, but it's too soon to tell anything."

"Oh my God," she whispered and turned her face away, crying helplessly. "Oh God, let him be all right, please just let him be all right."

The fundus nurse said, "Her uterus is contracted, doctor."

A minute later the placenta started to deliver, and Jean begged, "Please tell me how my baby is."

"We will," I said. "Just as soon as we know."

Dr. Orsini had the placenta in the container that goes over to the Path Lab. I checked to be sure it was intact.

"You're sterile," I said to him. "Go ahead and sew her up."

I went back to the table where the baby was lying. On each side of his head, a small oval depression showed where the forceps had been aligned. The nurse was cleaning off the whitish, cheeselike coating called vernix that covers newborns, while Dr. Rogan squeezed the oxygen bag and listened with his stethoscope. He looked up at me. "The heart's back around one thirty-five." Just then, the baby's legs suddenly flexed, his arms drew up against his chest and he started to fight the tube in his throat. Dr. Rogan and I exchanged a quick glance.

"I think we've got him," Dr. Rogan said.

We pulled the tube out and Jean's baby took two quick gulps of air and then let out a short loud bawl. Everyone in the room looked up. I don't know how many of us were there at that point. We listened for the next howl, which came loud and clear.

"Oh my God, I hear him, I can hear him," Jean cried.

Dr. Rogan brought their son over and put him on Jean's stomach. "He's a good little boy," he said.

Tears streamed down Jean's face as she held the baby against her. Ed was crying too, and the baby was howling, mouth gaping, eyes squinted tight, all red in the face, a gorgeous sight and sound.

Finally I said, "Don't you think we should all stop crying before we drown this little guy?" My voice sounded husky, even to me.

"I'm just so happy, Dr. Sweeney," Jean sobbed.

"Congratulations, both of you," I said.

Ed asked, "How much does he weigh?"

"Weigh? Who's had time to weigh him? As soon as you let go, we'll get around to that."

"Just a minute more," Jean pleaded. "Please."

I grinned. "He's your baby."

And then people started saying congratulations and leaving. The minute you get things under control, all your help is gone and nobody expects or waits for a thank-you. They've had their thanks.

6. Office Hours

It was nearly one when I got to the office. Several people were sitting in the waiting room. Katherine Donohue, my secretary, was on the phone. Our second line was lit and on "hold," while the third was ringing. I sometimes think the roughest part of my job falls on the poor secretary, who has to call everybody to cancel or reschedule appointments. That's why she asks for your phone number. People have to get baby-sitters and make all kinds of arrangements to come in, and then if the doctor's not here, they aren't very happy. The pregnant women will understand if I'm delivering someone. They may be next. But the gynecological ladies don't like it at all. And if it's hectic when I'm only late, imagine what it's like when I have to run out for a delivery in the middle of office hours.

I pulled a clean white coat from the closet. "The Simpsons had a boy," I told Katey Donohue when she hung up the phone.

She turned and grinned, then grabbed a stack of messages and followed me back to my office. "Sue Benning called twice," she said. "I know it's not an emergency, but she sounds upset."

"She's probably calling about her mother. Mrs. Benning didn't know she'd had a breast removed until I made rounds this morning."

"That must have been hard to tell her," Katey said.

"Don't feel sorry for me. She's the one had to hear it," I snapped, so Katey knew it had been rough. After ten years, she understands me. Without a good secretary a doctor is lost, and Mrs. Donohue is tops. "Let's try to get Sue on the phone before the madhouse starts here."

A minute later, Sue was on the line.

"It's pretty shitty, isn't it?" was her opening statement.

"Yeah, it is. Have you talked to Dr. Reis?"

"He came down after the operation yesterday and said he thought they got all the cancer out. I saw Mom this morning and she said you told her. She was sleeping when Dr. Reis made rounds last night."

"How was she feeling when you were there?"

"I'm not sure. She was quiet and didn't want to talk. I wish she would. I'm going back in a little while, and I guess I'm scared of how she's really taking it."

"Sue, I don't think anyone can tell you in advance how she'll take this. When you see her this afternoon, she may be more emotional. Let her cry if she wants to. She has to get it out. She has to face this thing."

Women react to a mastectomy in different ways. Some are bitter or angry at me, at the surgeon, at God. Others are stunned. "Why did this happen to me?" I think everybody must ask that question. And some are thankful and think we've saved their lives. I suppose in a way we have if we found the cancer early enough.

"Is your dad going to the hospital with you?"

"I don't know. He's at the office now."

There was a long pause, so I knew something else was

wrong. The husband is always among a woman's first thoughts. "Now I'm mutilated. How will he feel?" And you don't know how the husband will react. Even though he loves her, they've mutilated his wife, and that's hard for a man to accept. When I do a radical vulvectomy, take off a woman's vulva, that's a pretty repulsive-looking operation. There are some husbands who just can't take it and they walk out for good. But most husbands give all the support the wife needs.

"I tried to talk to Dad about it last night," Sue said. " 'It won't make that much difference, will it?' I asked him. Well, he didn't say anything for a long time—he was drinking a huge Scotch—and then he said, 'Don't worry.' But he wouldn't talk about it anymore."

Sue's voice had gotten very small, and if she'd been here, I'd have hugged her or tried to comfort her somehow. But over the phone I just told her I thought her mom and dad would eventually adjust and to let me know how things were going. She thanked me and we said good-bye. But neither of us felt very good.

I was just going in to see my first patient when Katey buzzed: "Dr. Sweeney, I've got a Mrs. Hemp on the phone. She's not one of our patients, but she says she has to talk to you. Will you take it?"

"Can't you find out what it's about?"

I don't generally take phone calls during office hours. Usually I can't, because I've got my hand in somebody's vagina. Of course if a doctor calls, I'll talk to him even if I have to come out of the examining room. And I've left patients on the table when our hospital line has rung and they've said, "Dr. Sweeney's needed *stat* in the operating room." *Stat* is medical shorthand from the Latin *statim,* meaning immediately. But once in a while if I'm not with a patient, when a woman says, "I have to talk to the doctor," I'll pick up. Maybe this is someone who's pregnant and single, and she doesn't care to tell the secretary that she wants an abortion. I can understand that. But other times, I'll pick up the phone and some woman who had to talk to me says, "I want to make an appointment."

"I don't make appointments," I'll tell her. "I work for the secretary. She makes the appointments." And I'll throw the hold down on the phone, buzz Katey and say, "Goddamit, all she wants is an appointment!"

Katey came back on the line. "Mrs. Hemp says she talked to you at home last night and you know what it's about."

"Oh my God, that idiot, I forgot about her. I don't want to talk to her. Just tell her I said not to dare come into this office."

"Whatever you say, Dr. Sweeney," Katey agreed smoothly, but she stayed on the intercom waiting for an explanation or for me to change my mind.

"Okay, I'll take it."

Mrs. Hemp had called at about 10 P.M. the night before. She had told the service it was an emergency. When she got me, she said I had to make a house call immediately.

"What for?" I asked.

"I'm pregnant and my husband and I spent the weekend with some friends and we just found out their son has German measles. I've got to have a doctor come over and look at me."

"What for?" I asked again.

"To tell me if I have German measles," she said, sounding as if she thought I was an imbecile. "I'm pregnant and if I have the German measles, I have to be aborted."

"Mrs. Hemp, I can't tell if you have German measles," I said, "because even if you got it this weekend, you're not going to have any symptoms for a few more days."

And oh, she'd been irate that I wouldn't make a house call. She wasn't even a patient of mine; she hadn't got around to registering yet.

So now she was phoning my office with her emergency,

saying she had been calling doctors all night and nobody would come to see her. "I want to come to your office for an examination," she said, "and I want you to tell your secretary she has to work me in today."

"Please *don't* come into my office, Mrs. Hemp," I pleaded. "Don't go to any obstetrician's office, just in case you do have German measles. Go to a pediatrician if you must. He's seen more German measles than anybody. Or go to an internist, but don't come here. We won't let you in if you come."

Suppose she *had* German measles. Suppose just for the sake of discussion that enough days had passed so she was infectious, and she walked into my consultation room with a dozen women in all stages of pregnancy. My God.

"I can see you don't want any new patients," she said furiously. "Well, I'll certainly spread the word around."

"Do that," I said and slammed down the phone.

I guess it was a way of letting out some of the tension after my conversation with Sue, but this was one woman I didn't want in any case. Naturally, we don't like to go around alienating patients, and I always tell the house staff: if you alienate a patient, you're not going to lose just that woman but the two she was going to tell and the four her friends were going to tell, and so on. But of course not everybody's going to like me, and I'm not going to like all of them, which is something most patients don't think about. I haven't ever said at the beginning of an interview, "I'm sorry, you're not for me," but I have told people that we clashed and they ought to go somewhere else. I'll always remember one woman: it was the day my son Jimmy went into a diabetic coma. We didn't even know he had diabetes. He had been sick and when I got to the hospital that morning, my wife was on the phone: Jimmy was comatose. So I roared home and brought him into the hospital and he came pretty close to dying. I was scheduled to have office hours and the girls had to cancel all the patients, but one woman gave my secretary a really hard time. "I have my office appointment and he's *going* to come and see me," she insisted. I called her later in the day and told her very frankly and succinctly to go to hell; she could find another doctor. If she couldn't have any compassion for my problems, then I could no longer take care of her. I'll never forget that woman. It's very rare for my personal life to interfere with my patients, but I have three sons, Bill, David and Jimmy, and I'd do anything including die for them if they needed me.

After the conversation with Mrs. Hemp, I went in to see my first patient. Partly to save time, I always start in the examining room. My nurse has taken the woman's pulse and blood pressure; the patient is undressed, wearing an examining gown and sitting on the table. Then I come in and take her history. It breaks the ice in a way. For a woman to come first into my office and then have to go get undressed—well, some of them are scared to death as it is. If we prolong their fright, by the time we get to the examining room they're shaking so hard I can't accomplish a thing.

In the examining room, I see the patient as a patient. Of course I'm aware if she's pretty, but that's not what I'm there for and her looks don't really come across. It's strictly clinical, with no sparks either way. And a nurse is always present; I won't work without one. I think it makes the patient feel more comfortable, but actually the nurse is there for my protection. It's very easy for a doctor to be caught alone with a woman who may be some sort of kook. He hasn't touched her, but if she starts screaming, "Rape!" he's vulnerable as hell. I mean, there's a lady lying naked and a man. She can claim anything. Unfortunately, some people really do take advantage of the examination situation. Not necessarily the doctor, either. I've had women I won't allow in my consultation room, let alone the examining room, without a nurse unless the door's open, because they'll be right over on my side of the desk. Besides, a doctor has to have a nurse present just in case he gets sued, to testify that everything was done correctly.

When a patient gets dressed and comes into my office, then I see her as a woman. I've just seen her naked and felt nothing, but now she sits across the desk from me with her skirt up above her knees, and I'm no longer just a doctor but a man, too. Women are much more attractive dressed than undressed, anyway. Sometimes I'll be writing my notes in a patient's chart and I'll put down, "Pretty as hell." And that's one reason no one sees my charts!

Mrs. Fremont was a new patient, a referral. She's married to a Frenchman whose business takes him back and forth between New York and San Francisco, but she had just spent two months in Tahiti. She was suntanned and attractive. Mrs. Fremont had a charming French accent. She told me there was no special problem—she and her husband didn't plan to have children—but she hadn't been examined in a couple of years. And the lady had never had a Pap smear.

"How come?" I asked.

"My doctor in San Francisco doesn't think they're necessary until a woman is thirty-five. I was just thirty-five, so I'm on time, I think."

"You're late as far as I'm concerned, Mrs. Fremont," I said, taking the smear and wondering who this doctor was. "I think every female who walks into a doctor's office ought to have a Pap smear. I don't care how old she is."

We've seen cancers in teen-age girls, and there are lots of cancers in twenty-year-olds. Early ones, though, that we can treat and cure. Every pregnant lady should have a Pap smear, too: the leading cause of *maternal* death at our hospital today is cancer.

"I think every woman should get a Pap test every six months," I told Mrs. Fremont. "A year is too long. Too many things can happen. The dentists really have it made. They've got the best public relations system in the world. You know,

'Brush your teeth twice a day; see your dentist twice a year.' And they've got people coming in like clockwork. Well, do you know anybody that died of cancer of the teeth? There is no cancer of the teeth. Yet we can hardly get all our patients to come in every year, much less every six months."

This is one of my pet subjects. It's not because I want to see more people. We send out bunches of notices reminding my patients their six-month visit is due. We don't know where we can put these women; we're busy enough as it is. But time is important if we're going to pick up the early little lesions and cure them. And you know, an obstetrician-gynecologist's head isn't down there in the pelvis, locked in. We look at the entire lady. While we don't do the complete examination an internist would take an hour to do, I think if a woman sees a gynecologist twice a year, she gets a pretty good checkup. Better in a way than with the internist, who conducts a meticulous examination of the heart and lungs but may not know what he's feeling in a pelvic exam.

While Mrs. Fremont dressed, I went into the second examining room to see Isabelle Cavallo. She was sitting on the table wearing one of the white paper gowns we use which open in front. She's twenty-six, a quiet, poised girl with black hair and almost black eyes. Her family is linked to the Spanish royal family. She was born and raised in this country, educated at convent schools, and eventually she married a young man who is also of Spanish descent. According to her chart, only five months had passed since her last checkup, and I wondered if she had come back early for some special reason.

I talked to her for a few minutes, asking about Luis— they've been married three years—and I was kind of fishing to see if something was on her mind, but she didn't say anything. She didn't mention pregnancy and neither did I.

My nurse Laura McKay came in, and I went ahead and listened to Isabelle's heart and lungs, examined the abdomen and thyroid and breasts and did a thorough examination of the ovaries, uterus, vagina and rectum. And of course I took a Pap smear.

Back in my office I spoke briefly to Mrs. Fremont, and then made a couple of notes in Isabelle's chart while I waited for her.

After fifteen or twenty years in the business, a doctor develops an instinct for when a patient has something on her mind. Sometimes it's just a hunch; other times there'll be a clue. Take the woman who comes in for a so-called gynecological problem—vaginal discharge, for example. I examine her and find there's nothing unusual or wrong. But then, after we've settled in my office, the truth comes pouring out. Often it's the fact that she's been unfaithful. And she's got to tell somebody. If she can't talk about it, there's not much fun in doing it. She can't tell her husband, certainly, and she doesn't really want to tell her friends. Maybe she could talk to her minister or priest or rabbi, but he's going to judge, and she knows I'm not. I won't say, "You were a bad girl"; or "Give me a thousand dollars and I'll declare you free of sin."

She feels a little guilty and yet she's elated. It's kind of nice for her ego to know she's attractive to someone else. And she'll talk about everything—not only when and how, but with whom.

I feel sorry for a lot of women whose marriages are at the point where they have to resort to affairs for their kicks. On the other hand, as far as marriage is concerned, if it ain't good in bed, *it ain't good*. And if we accept that a man can have an affair, then why can't a woman? I think that double standard is a lot of nonsense.

Isabelle Cavallo entered my office and sat down with trained grace. I told her the examination was fine and then asked, "Isabelle, is there anything you'd like to talk about?" It was the first time I'd called her by her first name. I thought it would make things less formal.

Finally, after much hemming and hawing, she said she'd like to ask a question.

"What is it?"

"It's about intercourse."

"What about it?"

"Well, I enjoy it, and I think everything is pretty good, Dr. Sweeney, but I'm just not sure. I think I sometimes have an orgasm, but I don't really know."

Now, she was twenty-six years old, and when she was married, both Isabelle and her husband were virgins. So here were these two relatively "old" people, if you will, but neither of them with any other experience.

I asked her what she and Luis did during intercourse. They had been going through all the motions: clitoral stimulation with the tongue as well as with the finger. But finally the other day she'd admitted to Luis that she had been faking the orgasm. And after three years of marriage, he said to her, "I'm not sure where your clitoris *is*." She admitted she didn't know either, whereupon Luis suggested that if she could get up enough nerve, she should ask her doctor.

So this girl had really come to find out where her clitoris was. And we had to get her all undressed and go back to the examining room and with a mirror show her where her clitoris was located. She didn't know what the urethra was, either: the little opening from the bladder that's just under the clitoris. She had never learned anything about her anatomy, and neither had he. Probably now, knowing where things are, and being able to talk honestly about it, sex will be much more satisfying for them. At least I hope so.

My next patient, Mrs. Walters, had come to see me because of a vaginal itch. I suppose vaginal discharge and itch are the most common problems a gynecologist treats. It's easy to laugh or say, "Oh my God, here comes another itchy twat!" But it's awful to itch, especially there. You can't scratch your vagina on the bus coming here. And when you're itching, intercourse isn't any fun; it hurts. We examine these patients and take cultures to see what's causing the problem and then treat it. We may prescribe something for the husband, too, if we think he might be reinfecting his wife.

Vaginal itch can be a damn difficult thing to get rid of. All of us have sinuses but only certain people are susceptible to sinus attacks. And all women have vaginas but only certain ones have these attacks. The woman who has sinusitis knows it can come back. She just treats it again and doesn't get angry. But the lady who has vaginitis wants to be treated once and cured. If it does come back, as it did with Mrs. Walters, she's furious.

Tuesday was an average office day until midafternoon. Most people come for routine examinations, that's all. They're pregnant, or have just delivered, or want contraception, or they saw the poster in the subway saying "Get a Pap test." People are usually sick when they go to an internist or surgeon, but in general they're well when they come to a gynecologist or an obstetrician. So ours is a different business to start with.

An average obstetrician-gynecologist in New York City probably sees between thirty and fifty patients a day. My secretary generally makes my appointments every fifteen minutes for gynecological patients, and every five or ten minutes for obstetrical ladies because I'm checking them so frequently and their visits are usually routine.

But at 3:30 in the afternoon, I spent a full hour with Kim Ungar, shot my schedule all to hell and didn't give a damn. Kim is sixteen and I had to tell her she had cancer of the vagina. Mrs. Ungar had been given stilbestrol, an artificial estrogen, when she was pregnant with Kim. Stilbestrol had proved effective in preventing some threatened miscarriages, but it was subsequently found to cause cancer. Now, Kim was among the small percentage of victims, usually teenagers, who were developing cancer of the vagina because their mothers had been treated with this hormone.

Kim had been accompanied to the office by her mother, but Mrs. Ungar was so filled with guilt and despair that she just sat silent and stricken while Kim alternately cried and screamed furiously, cursing doctors and their ignorance and life in general. I sat and listened. She had to let it out on someone. And I didn't blame her. We were going to have to remove her vagina and uterus, and she was sixteen years old. I told her I would do plastic surgery and make her a new vagina. "I don't want to live that way," she screamed. "I don't want to live at all." She threatened to kill herself. She said she was sorry she hadn't slept with every boy she'd ever dated. Then she cried some more. Eventually she asked one or two questions about the operation.

At one point Katey buzzed because I had an office full of patients. I told her they could wait or come back.

Finally Kim asked whether she would be able to continue ice-skating after the operation. She wanted to be a professional figure skater. I said she could skate all she wanted as soon as she was better. A little while later, she and her mother left.

The routine patients resumed, but Kim stayed in my mind, and I knew she would be there for a long time. For the next couple of hours I was glad to see nothing more serious than a woman who was bleeding again between menstrual periods. Fortunately her tests had all come back negative. She and her husband were Catholic, and although she occasionally used a diaphragm and he sometimes used a condom, they felt guilty about doing something the Church was against. She didn't want another baby yet, but he was one of those guys who always wanted to be in bed—the big lover and he-man bit. And he wanted to live a little dangerously and not use any contraceptive. Vatican roulette.

"It's all very nice and fun," she said to me, "but too much is too much of anything." So she bleeds all the time and then refuses him.

I'd examined her and done tests before and been unable to find anything wrong, so the question was whether she was bleeding as a means of keeping her husband away. I decided not to do a D and C this time. A D and C, or dilatation and curettage, is a relatively minor surgical procedure in which we dilate the cervix and scrape out the inside of the uterus. I said, "I don't want you to have intercourse without protection." That's what she wanted to be told anyway, and maybe hearing it from her doctor would help.

Another girl was having periods only once or twice a year. After the examination I started her on a BBT or basal body temperature chart to find out whether she was ovulating and arranged to have her come back for further tests.

I saw three pregnant women and a sixteen-year-old girl who wanted contraceptive pills. I gave them to her. If a young kid comes in here requesting contraception, I think she'd better get it. I don't ask for parents' consent because most sixteen-year-olds don't want their parents to know they need birth control. Besides, New York State law authorizes this medical service for persons sixteen or over without parental consent. Sometimes a mother brings a very young girl to get contraception, and I think that takes a lot of love. It's awful to admit to yourself that your sweet little fourteen-year-old daughter is in bed with somebody, but it's better to face that than her pregnancy.

Then, as my last patient Tuesday afternoon, I saw Mavis Rogers. I really like Mavis, but as usual, I was scared of what I might find when I examined her. This woman's sister and mother both died of cancer of the ovary. In fact, her grandmother and a maternal aunt died that way, too.

Ovarian cancer is a highly malignant disease which usually

doesn't have any advance symptoms. By the time we found it in Mavis's sister Edith she had fluid in her abdomen and nodules in her pelvis. She was thirty-seven years old, with one child. We took her to the hospital and when we operated, just a week after she first noticed her stomach was larger than normal, she had advanced carcinoma of the ovary. Sometimes we can't do anything surgically because the cancer has spread everywhere and it's a friable sort of lesion, that is, it crumbles. We don't want to cut through cancer if we can avoid it because it will spread. So in some cases, we open the patient, look around and then just close. With Edith, we managed to remove the ovaries and uterus and omentum, which is a fat pad in the abdomen, and a tumor in her upper abdomen beneath the diaphragm. We took out everything we could and gave her intra-abdominal radioactive phosphorus as well as postoperative X-ray. But she'd had 3,000 cc's of fluid in her abdomen when we opened it—three liters of fluid—and we all knew she didn't have long to live. Ten months after we operated her tumor recurred and we started her on chemotherapy, but by then she was nauseated and vomiting. Edith died a few months later.

Mavis Rogers is a large—I guess you'd have to say fat— woman, with bright red hair and a big sunny face. I delivered her two children, and now she was thirty-five, not planning to have any more babies, and I wanted her to have her ovaries taken out. They were normal as far as I knew, but with her family's history of ovarian cancer, I thought we should remove them before anything happened. But Mavis said no. She'd been refusing to be operated on for about a year. Her whole family wanted her to have it done. I called her husband to see if he could put some pressure on her, but he said, "You're the doctor and she won't listen to *you*. She listens to me even less. I wish to God there was something I could do."

So Mavis came in to be examined every two or three months. Each visit I would ask her, "What are you waiting for?"

And she would lean back in the chair in my office, big, red-haired and stubborn, stare at me and say, "I'm not waiting *for* anything. I just don't want to. I'm a woman and I'm not ready to stop being one."

I would tell her that was a bunch of baloney, she wasn't going to stop being a woman if she had her ovaries removed. She would reply, "When I want to be castrated, you'll be the first to know." Then suddenly she would smile and tell me something funny about her kids or her job—she's a department store buyer for junior-petite sizes, which she calls "the epitome of wishful thinking"—and that way she would simply close the subject.

During this visit I gave it one more try.

She said, "Don't you get tired of this subject, Dr. Sweeney?"

"I want a reason from you that makes sense."

"I just don't want to."

"Look, Mavis, it may be psychologically awful to have your ovaries out. But isn't it worse to come back here every few months when one day I may have to say, 'I'm sorry, it's your turn now,' and you'll know that you will be *dead* in six months or a year?"

Mavis stared at me. "You worry too much, Dr. Sweeney," she said. "If you don't watch out, you're going to get an ulcer."

7. A Demanding Mistress

Office hours ended at 7 P.M. Tuesday. I skipped a lot of phone calls and dinner and rushed through rounds because I had a PTA meeting to go to. Once I thought I'd never get stuck with those again, but when I remarried, my wife Fran had two children, Brett and Michelle. Before that, when people discussed adoption and said, "Oh, I couldn't love it the same way, it wouldn't be my own child," I always answered, "Isn't that ridiculous? Why can't you love somebody else's kid just as much as your own? After a while it will really be yours anyway." But I didn't know how true that statement was until Brett and Michelle. They can say or do something so touching that I'll get all teary. I cry a lot. I cry at weddings and births. I'm a real slob.

I'm a softy as far as women are concerned, too. You hear that obstetricians or gynecologists are in the business because they hate women. It's certainly possible that some doctors like to see women suffer, and motivation like that really worries me. On the other hand, when they say the patient falls in love with her obstetrician they should add that an obstetrician falls in love with his patient, too. This is not a sexual feeling I'm talking about. But obstetricians really know their patients. My God, we probably learn more about these women than their husbands or families or anyone. I mean, why lie to me? They tell me everything. When I've been seeing a pregnant lady for seven or eight months and then I deliver her baby, at the end she's crying and her husband's crying and I'm hugging this girl and I'm madly in love with her at that point. There are lots of them I love.

I always wanted to be a doctor, even when I was a little boy. Then along came World War II. So when I finished college I had to go to war, fly the B-17's and do the other crap that war requires. But as soon as I came back, I began medical school.

I can remember making the decision to go into obstetrics and gynecology. I was in my third year of Cornell University Medical College, and I went up to watch a delivery. I'd never seen one before. I can still remember the room where I was sitting. I'd never been so excited in my life. I came walking out of there and said, "That's it!" I went home and told my wife I wanted to be an obstetrician-gynecologist.

"Oh *no*," she said. "The one thing I didn't want you to be!"

Because you're always on call. Your life isn't your own. People have to be a little crazy to go into medicine in the first place, but obstetrics is a hell of a way to make a living, even for a doctor. That was it, though. Obstetrics and gynecology had everything I wanted. I liked surgery, but I didn't like the general surgeon's distant or cold approach. As a gynecologist I could do surgery without forfeiting the physician's relationship with his patients. And I loved the fun of obstetrics.

Most people probably don't realize that all medical students deliver babies. The experience is usually the highlight of a student's medical-school career even if he doesn't want to go into obstetrics. For one thing it's the first time he's been called Doctor. The title is used for the patient's sake. The student acts like a doctor and the patient thinks he's a doctor. *He* thinks he's a doctor! I remember when it happened to me. The attending obstetrician kept saying, "Doctor, doctor, doctor. Dr. *Sweeney.*" I finally said, "You mean *me?*" I'd always been called Mister. Of course we were under close supervision. Nobody ever turned us loose with a patient. But it was tremendous.

Cornell Medical College is affiliated with The New York Hospital, where the medical student gets his first contact with patients. Along with the endless work and study, details and pressure, he has a lot of experiences he'll remember forever.

I'll never forget a huge Irish woman named Bridie. She weighed about 230 pounds, and she was in labor. I remember Bridie because there I was, a fourth-year medical student, prancing around like the big doctor. I was sent in to examine Bridie, who was so large I had to get up on a stand next to the bed to reach her. She was lying with her big legs spread apart, and I was in there trying to tell how far she was dilated. I couldn't feel a thing. I was pushing and probing to find the opening of the cervix, but I still couldn't feel anything. And all of a sudden, she reached around—she was lying there flat in the bed—and she got me right by the seat of the pants and picked me up off the stand so I was dangling in the air, feet kicking away. And she said to me in a strong Irish accent, "Okay, *sonny*, that's long enough!" I was never so embarrassed in my life. I was crushed.

Fat people are often quite memorable. I remember patients so huge you couldn't tell they were pregnant. I saw a woman bring her fourteen-year-old daughter into the emergency room with acute abdominal pain recurring every five minutes. This kid was in labor and her mother didn't even know she was pregnant. She delivered safely, but I don't know what her mother did to her afterward.

I remember a black woman who was so fat she couldn't fit in the telephone booth in the hospital. She had to stand outside in the hall to call home. She was a clinic patient and she had to come to the hospital in one of those Checker cabs; she wouldn't fit in a little one, and she couldn't get on the bus. She was so big that we had to put two beds together in the hospital and she slept across them.

Short of X-rays or tests, there was no way in the world to tell whether that woman was pregnant or in labor; you couldn't feel anything, she was so huge. Her thighs were as big around as lamp shades. I don't know how she *got* pregnant. And this obesity was a strain on her heart. But she wouldn't do what we told her. She was mean, too. We told her to stay in bed, and we'd find her out in the hall talking on the phone.

We'd say, "Mrs. So-and-so, you have high blood pressure, we told you to stay in bed."

And she'd glower at us and say, "Yeah? Shit."

Finally I said, "Okay, we can't handle her, I'll talk to her husband and see what he can do." I was expecting a great big six-foot-four hulk of a man, and down the hall, click, click, click, came this little guy—he must have been about five foot two. I don't know how he got her pregnant, how he ever found the right place, let alone impregnated her. I explained she wasn't doing what we told her. And he whirled into the room where that six-foot woman was, shaking his finger at her, yelling and absolutely laying down the law. And she just kept saying, "Yes dear, yes dear." I remember it so well, him with his little moustache, bristling from head to toe. And she was good after that. Still mean, but good.

There was a guy in my class in medical school who wanted

to be an actor. He was tall and handsome with thick dark hair, and he "tahlked" like an actor in deep, round, stentorian tones. When he spoke to a patient, he would call her Mother, and things like that. He wasn't too well liked by the people on the staff and they were always trying to figure out ways to make him look like an ass. One day they set him up. Right across from the nurses' station was a private room where a woman had just *died*, and they sent Arthur in to take her history. He didn't know she was dead. They left the door open and told him that she was a little hard of hearing.

So in went Arthur. "Good morning, Mother."

No response.

"Good morning, Mother."

And he launched into his act, trying to take a history from this dead woman while the entire staff watched from across the hall. Finally he realized he'd been set up, and he came slinking out.

Some incidents at medical school aren't very funny. Once Arthur and I were sent to do a test on a man who had high blood pressure. The patient was more dead than alive. He had uremia, and when you die of uremia, you get a sort of icing around your mouth called uremic frost. We were supposed to do a circulation time on this man: inject something called magnesium sulphate into his vein and see how long it took for him to tell us he could taste it. The nurse gave us the stuff and Arthur and I went in and hooked him up. We shot him with the magnesium sulphate and *"Yeeipe"*— he started to scream, "My God, I'm on fire, I'm on *fire!*"

So of course Arthur said in his most dramatic basso, "Good heavens, man, it's merely a bit of burning, what are you talking about, you're on fire?"

We did it again; and he started yelling he was on fire. Arthur and I looked at each other. It wasn't supposed to be like that; he was just supposed to get a little burning taste in his mouth.

We went out to the nurse and said, "What did you give us to inject?"

Now, we should have looked. Before a doctor ever injects anything, he should check the vial the nurse took it from. Well, she found the vial. We were supposed to have given him a 5 percent magnesium sulphate and we had used 50 percent magnesium sulphate. I looked at Arthur. He looked at me. Over in pharmacology we used to *kill* rabbits by injecting them with 50 percent magnesium sulphate. We went roaring into the room and there the man sat and he said: "Jesus Christ, doc, if only it didn't burn so much, I haven't felt this good in years!"

We had brought his blood pressure right down to normal with that dosage. If he'd had a normal blood pressure, we would have killed him. Instead, his uremic frost was gone, his headache was gone, he was fine for a little while. But I learned a lesson. Since then, I have never injected anything without seeing where it came from.

A lot of things happen when you're a medical student or an intern, and you can't always be prepared. As an intern, I was sent to see a private patient who had just had a vaginal operation. She lithped a little when she talked.

"Dr. Thweeney," she said, "what I want to know ith, when can I have intercourth?"

"You just had your operation yesterday."

"Oh," she said, "yeth, I know, but my puthy's jutht a-twitching!"

This was my first experience with something like that. I couldn't help laughing, and oh my, I kind of roared out of the room.

Anyway, by the end of my four years at medical school, I was more certain than ever that I wanted to be this strange breed of doctor with the triple role: obstetrician, gynecologist and gynecological surgeon. But I didn't know if I'd be any good. Particularly in surgical specialties, a student learns all the theories but he lacks the practical experience of applying them to a patient. It's very easy to read about how to do a hysterectomy, but it's a different matter when suddenly it's your turn to pick up the knife. A medical student has never operated on anyone; he wasn't a doctor then. He may have scrubbed and assisted in surgery and held the retractors or hooks. Or he may have done a D and C, a dilatation and curettage, which is a relatively minor surgical procedure involving no cutting. But after he graduates with his MD, this young doctor still has to learn to operate. And unfortunately, whom does he have to learn on? Patients. We got a little experience operating on dogs or other animals, and although this will probably stir up feelings among animal lovers, I don't think a surgeon should be turned loose on someone's wife or mother or baby unless he's had that practice. None of these animals was butchered. We did everything in a regular operating room with sterile precautions, and if you walked in, you wouldn't have known whether it was an animal or a human having the surgery. But the time comes when a young doctor has to do these things for real, on a human patient. And he's got to make his mistakes. Every surgeon has made them.

My first operation was on an ovarian cyst. I can well remember that. Of course there was a senior doctor scrubbed and standing there right across from me. I was an intern and had assisted at operations before. I would watch the surgeon work and there was nothing to it; I figured I could do that without any problem. When I went to do my own first operation, I didn't even realize I was tense—I was God's gift to American surgery at that point. But I probably never moved my head during the entire ninety minutes of operating, and my neck was so stiff at the end that I couldn't even turn to walk away from the table.

So a new intern doesn't know whether he's good. Often he doesn't even know what he wants to specialize in. That's why there are rotating internships, where a doctor works in a number of different disciplines—medicine, surgery, pediatrics, and so forth—not only to gain experience, but often to decide what he really wants to be in life.

I spent my internship year, from July, 1949, to July, 1950, in New York Hospital's Department of Obstetrics and Gynecology. I was twenty-eight and married, which was very unusual in those days. Today, most young doctors are married, and most of the house staff, which includes interns and residents, lives across the street from the hospital. But back then, we weren't allowed to go across the street. We had to be in the building, so I slept in the hospital when I was on duty—which was most of the time. I can remember being severely chastised once by the head of the department. He was chewing me out for something and I protested, "But I wasn't here last night. I was off." He said, "What do you mean, you were off? You take the job here, you work twenty-four hours a day, seven days a week, you're *never off.*" The kids today are always off. At five o'clock, you can't find them in the hospital. They just don't want to work the way we did.

As a resident, a doctor has a unique chance to continue working in his specialty surrounded by more senior men who can advise or help him when he needs it. And by the time he is in his third or fourth year of residency, he in turn is teaching the younger doctors or medical students.

When I was a third-year resident, a medical student came down to Gynecological Clinic, where I was working. He had a voice that you could hear all over the clinic, and his patient was a little old lady who talked in a murmur. He was taking her history and the conversation I overheard went something like this:

He said, "You have to do *what?*"

The little voice said, "Bzz zzz."

"*Well, where do you put it?*" asked the student.

Finally having finished his questions, he ushered the lady

into the examining room. Now this was his first time in GYN clinic, and to make matters worse, he had a student nurse with him who was equally inexperienced. Anyway, they got the woman up on the table properly covered with a sheet, her feet in the stirrups and her buttocks down at the end of the table. And now he was ready to examine her. Of course he was playing doctor like we all did in medical school; but when he threw back the sheet, he took one look and just said, "Oh my God!" The nurse looked and didn't say a word. They dropped the sheet over her and came running out to get me.

It turned out that this patient had a prolapsed uterus—her uterus had come all the way down and was hanging out of her vagina. In retrospect, what this student had asked her first was, "What is the problem?"

And she had answered, "I have to put my womb away at night."

"You have to do *what*?"

"I have to put my womb away at night."

"*Well, where do you put it?*" As though she had a choice!

Then, when they lifted the sheet in the examining room, they'd never seen anything like this in their lives, so they just covered her and he came racing over to me and said, "You wouldn't believe what I just saw." He's a gynecologist now, and every once in a while I'll still kid him and say, "Well, where do *you* put it?"

One thing that stands out in my memories about residency is the money problem I faced. When I was a resident at New York Hospital, my salary was $25 a month. That was after four years of college, three years in the army, four years of medical school and a year of internship. Then I was a resident for four years, and at the age of thirty-three, as Chief Resident in Obstetrics and Gynecology, I was paid $1,000 a year.

I remember one day I bumped into the Chief Surgical

Resident in the operating room. At that time, the surgical residency lasted seven years, and I asked this guy, "How can you manage?"

He shrugged. "I'm in debt $25,000."

"You're out of your mind," I said. "I'm not going to do that."

Four years later, I owed $25,000 just like everybody else. I couldn't live on $1,000 a year; I was married and my first two sons had been born, so I borrowed to live. And there I was, in my midthirties, deeply in debt, and I hadn't seen my first private patient yet.

My first job was with a group of doctors in practice in a small community in northern Connecticut. I went there because I thought it was a good place to raise children, and because in group practice there wouldn't be that awful wait for the first patient to come through the door. And the money, I thought, was great. It wasn't great, but after what I had been earning, when they offered me $10,000 a year, I figured I was on easy street.

One of the things I remember well about that year was the first patient I saw after I joined the group. She was an old lady who had brought in her daughter, and the thing I remember was her asking me, "How much is the visit going to be?"

Now, I'd been out of medical school five years, but I'd never charged anybody anything, because at the hospital I'd only seen clinic patients. *I* didn't know what I was supposed to charge her. And I was embarrassed. I'd never had to talk about prices and I didn't know how to do it. You know, in academic medicine, money's a dirty word. What I finally blurted to this woman was, "I guess it'll be five dollars, how about that!"

I not only said five dollars, I said, "Five dollars, how about *that*?" She was a nice old lady, but it's a wonder she just didn't slap my face, or say "How about two ninety-five?" Oh

God, I was so embarrassed. Today I laugh about it, but then, nobody had ever taught me. I didn't know how to handle it.

I had a medical student in my office one night recently, asking my opinion about residencies and private practice, and I said, "They ought to have a course on how to run an office. And they ought to make students come to an office and find out how it really works. I mean, you don't know what to charge, what's reasonable, or how to say it. Even now I don't like to talk about money. If a patient asks me about the charge, I say, 'Go talk to the secretary. She takes care of that part of it.' "

I returned to New York City after a year in Connecticut because practice in a small community was kind of frustrating to me medically. In a town where everyone knows what everyone else is doing, a doctor can't afford any mistakes or problems. He won't last long. As a result, some doctors send their tough cases to the city. They can't risk a complication. This is especially true in cancer work. The patient will accept the same complication from us in the city that she wouldn't accept from her small-town doctor. After all, she's come to mecca, where the experts are. She's overwhelmed by the size of the hospital and by the fact that there are a lot of people there with the same problem. That doesn't mean the doctor in her town isn't as good as the city doctor. He may have trained at the same hospital. But he's running a different show. And if he doesn't handle certain kinds of cases for a while, he may come to feel that he's *not* as well qualified, so he'll send them to us and say, "You're doing this, do it." I think it takes a pretty honest guy to make that decision.

Another frustrating thing about the practice of medicine in a small community is that like it or not, what's done in the community is what you're going to do. Take the old obstetrical dictum, "Once a Caesarean, always a Caesarean," meaning once a patient has had a delivery by Caesarean section, all of her subsequent deliveries have to be this way. The dictum is wrong, and I was trained in a place where we did *not* do Caesarean sections just because somebody had had one before, unless the reason for the Caesarean was recurrent, like a tiny pelvis. Well, I came out of residency highly trained, all starry-eyed and bushy-tailed, prepared to let these women labor. After all, I'd let them labor at the "mother" hospital and they'd delivered with no trouble. But not up there. If I'd ever allowed a lady with a uterine scar from a previous Caesarean section to go into labor and then she ruptured her uterus or got into trouble of any kind, I'd have been finished right then. So regardless of what I knew, I had to acquiesce to the community's way of medicine.

It sounds like I'm saying we're right and they're wrong. And medically, our way of doing things may be correct. But there are other factors. Take New York Hospital, where I was trained: there was a full complement of house officers, some twenty-plus young doctors, available all the time. A small community doctor may have only two interns, often foreigners schooled abroad, not fluent in English to help him. We had operating rooms, X-ray machines, even a blood bank right on the delivery floor. We had constant attendance of the patient by either a medical student, doctor or nurse. We could operate any time, day or night, and even convert a delivery room into an operating room. In an emergency, we could be operating within ten minutes. At the Connecticut hospital, there were three full operating rooms not only distinct from the delivery suite but down the hall, up two flights of stairs, around the next wing and down another hall. And when you got your patient there, you found a general surgeon taking out somebody's stomach in one room, a hip being pinned in the second room and a hysterectomy half finished in the third. There you were with a ruptured uterus and no place to operate. Besides, where I trained, the staff in the delivery room included a medical student or intern or both, a resident, a nurse, a circulating nurse, an anesthetist and me. Up there, we had the nurse and me, that was all. She was the anesthetist, the fundus nurse, the circulating nurse, my obstetrical assistant—and she answered the phone if it rang. Under those circumstances, how could I prove my point? What was I trying to prove? That somebody could deliver from below? If she did, and everything went well, fine. But if she didn't, I was going to lose the mother as well as the baby in that setup. So maybe their medicine was the best thing for them. It was just unfulfilling for me.

Another reason I returned to New York was that I missed a teaching hospital, where somebody would question what I was doing. A doctor can get so he thinks he's perfect. That's one of the things most doctors' wives would change about us first. Well, they're right: we all tend to think we're perfect. And we've got to be in most ways. I used to say when people complained about the Yankees always winning, *"What's wrong with winning?"* In my business there's no room to lose. Yet we're human, so we'll make mistakes. The good, stimulating thing about a medical center is that the students or house staff will ask, "Why did you do that?" You have to justify what you did. The real holier-than-thou guy is the doctor in the little hospital with nobody to check on him.

Just the other morning I was operating on a woman who had a big tumor growing out of her uterus, pushing all her organs out of place. I reached in and pulled the tumor through the incision so I could look at it. It must have weighed a couple of pounds and it was as big as a melon. I said, "Beautiful. It looks like a myoma." Which is a benign tumor composed of muscular tissue.

If you've never seen a tumor, it's only beautiful if you were afraid it was going to be malignant and then it turns out to be benign. This kind of tumor looks like it's trying to burst the semitransparent covering around it. It's a little like one of those precooked tongues that come in a plastic boil-in-the-sac, only it's a whitish color if it's a myoma, and

it's absolutely solid. So then you've got to go into the uterus
—forget the bleeding for the moment—get within the cap-
sule of the tumor and shell it right out.

I said to the anesthesiologist, "Can you tip her a little? I
can't get at this too well."

He tipped the operating table back, so her head and shoulders went lower. Then the resident said, "You're *not* going
to do a hysterectomy? You're just going to take the myoma
off?"

"She's twenty-nine, unmarried, no children," I answered.
"*No,* we're not going to do a hysterectomy if this is what it
looks like. She's still got a normal uterus and may want to
have kids."

So we cut the tumor out, put it in a pan and a pathologist
sliced through it much the way you'd slice a loaf of bread,
to see if it was fibroid and benign all the way through, without any yellowish color inside. Fortunately it was, and there's
no reason this woman can't have children someday. The
point I'm trying to make is, I want to hear the questions from
the house staff and students, partly for myself and mostly
because I'm teaching, and I enjoy that.

Finally, I left Connecticut because I didn't like working in
a group. I didn't want to practice medicine from nine to five.
I wanted to know and deliver my own patients, not have
them referred to another doctor who was covering that night
or weekend. For me, it was worth paying the price to be in
private practice.

The price you have to pay is time. There are lots of things
that normal people do that we just don't get to. I don't think
I've seen the inside of a bank in years. My secretary has to
go to the bank and I get my money from her. It's even a big
production to get a haircut. There are weeks when I'll want
to go and can't. In the days when short hair was the style for
men, mine would grow and grow and people would start re-
marking about the doctor with the long hair! The same with

the dentist: I make three or four appointments and may get to keep one. Then I sit in the dentist's chair and *his* phone rings and *his* secretary is taking my messages. I've had to leave for a delivery with a tooth half filled.

But the highest price, and what a doctor regrets most, is missing so much of his family life. The problem with the young obstetrician isn't that he doesn't *want* to go home to his family, but that he *can't* go home. Especially if he starts out with no money at all—in debt to begin with—and no source of income except his own hands and brain. Not only does he have to pay off his debts, but it costs him another $25,000 to open an office, so he has to work. And he loves his work. He gets swept up in it.

I think all wives and kids resent it if Daddy's not there much. Any successful person has the same problem. A good garage mechanic has to spend a great deal of time at the garage or else he's not a good mechanic. But something has to give. Unfortunately, the family life suffers for your professional life. And this business of being a doctor is perhaps more demanding than most.

Then when I do go home, I'm either cranky or dead tired, and sometimes I flop into bed or go to sleep at the dinner table. Or tonight's the theater event we've been waiting for all month and we can't go because the phone rings. Or we go and have to leave in the middle. Or we get there and I fall sound asleep.

And there are times I go home depressed. That's another problem with being a doctor's wife: we take things home with us. Suppose a woman dies on the operating table. We're just as human as the next guy—or more so. This was our patient. People say, "Oh, the doctors and nurses are immune. They see it all the time." How can you be hardened to somebody's dying? Or to an abnormal baby?

After I've delivered an abnormal child, I go home knowing the mother is likely to wake up the next morning and hope or even believe it was all a bad dream, that her baby will be brought in perfectly healthy. But I know her baby's never going to be fine. So that night I go home depressed for this lady—and perhaps I'm also feeling a little guilt. That's probably the mother's first emotion—guilt: what did she do wrong? And if as a doctor I can say her hangup is perfectly normal, then I have to accept the same hangup in myself. There's always the fleeting thought, "If only I had told her *not* to take the aspirin . . . or the trip . . . or something else. Might it have made a difference?" My wife may try to comfort me but she can't, really, and it must be awfully hard for a woman to know there are times when she's simply unable to get through to her husband. Recently Fran, doing her best to be reassuring and get me out of my depression, said, "It wasn't your fault. Even if it had been, you can't expect yourself to be perfect." I looked at her and said, "If I were operating on you, you'd want me to be perfect, wouldn't you?"

Even on the good nights, a doctor is waiting for something to happen. There's no such thing as being finished with work. He's always available, always in touch with his service. When I go to my PTA meeting, I take my beeper with me. This gadget is about the size of a little transistor radio, and I clip it to my inside jacket pocket. Actually, there are smaller beepers, but I prefer mine because a little one wouldn't talk to me, it would just beep. So if I were driving down the East River Drive in traffic and that damn thing went off and I didn't know what the problem was, I'd be rushing like mad to get off the Drive and find the nearest phone. Then I'd call in and the service might say my wife just wanted me to stop on the way home and pick up something from the drugstore for her hair. At least the model I have tells me what the story is. A woman operator records the message and then it's repeated until I turn the beeper off. But initially it makes a lot of noise to get your attention: sort of a huge three-toned

Beep-Beep Boop *Bleep*. It's ear piercing when it's turned on loud.

One evening we were at the Repertory Theater in Lincoln Center. It's a relatively small place with these little half-steps going down the aisles. Well, right in the middle of the play, this thing went off. Inadvertently I'd turned it way up, and in the dark I couldn't find the button to shut it off. In order to stop the racket, I started to leave, at which point I fell *up* those little steps. There I was, lying prone, with this thing still going, making all the noise in the world. My wife wouldn't even sit with me, she was so embarrassed.

I guess being a doctor's wife is about the toughest job in the world. I won't let my daughter Michelle marry a doctor if I can help it. I always speak of medicine and especially obstetrics as a demanding mistress. I don't have an ordinary mistress, but my medical mistress is more demanding than any woman could be. And a wife could no more help being jealous of that mistress than of a real one. Something else is taking an awful lot of her husband's emotion and attention, day and night.

And we're constantly working with women. After a while a wife understands that the doctor-patient relationship is never sexual. But we get phone calls from women all the time. Letters and flowers and gifts arrive. We're little gods. And we get to be spoiled.

It's not just that we're idolized by our patients. We also work in offices and hospitals where we're waited on. Especially as surgeons, we don't get anything for ourselves: the nurse hands us the instruments or whatever we need. We drop a white coat and a nurse picks it up. If you drop your socks at home, is your wife going to want to run around collecting them? We never clean anything. When we operate, somebody else washes all the instruments. If, God forbid, a scalpel is dirty, we throw it at a nurse and say, "This one's *dirty!* How *come* this one's dirty?" Do that at home with a fork or knife and your wife has a right to kill you!

So we're tough to live with because we're spoiled. And we're egotistical. It's an egotistical thing to become a doctor in the first place, to think you're competent to take other people's lives in your hands. Yet every single day we make decisions that affect people's lives. And to top it all off, we enjoy it. Don't let anybody tell you that a doctor doesn't *enjoy* the work, the success and the adoration he gets. He does. He really loves that mistress.

8. Very Special Women

One morning near the end of May, Katey, my secretary, stopped me on the way into the examining room. "Dr. Sweeney, I've got Mrs. Merrill on the phone. Will you talk to her?"

She knew Betsy was one of my favorites and I grinned and said, "Yes," and went back to my office.

Betsy was an infertility patient. She had come to me nearly a year before because she and her husband Alex had been trying to have a child and she hadn't been able to conceive. Finally they had admitted to themselves that something might be wrong with one of them. Just to sit down and face that fact together takes a lot of guts and love. Then to have to bring the problem to a stranger, tell me all about their sex life and emotional relationship, requires real courage. But after I had examined Betsy, she sat in my office and in a voice shaking with tension, plowed her way through a detailed description of their efforts to have a baby. I hardly had to ask a question. I remember she was holding a slip of paper on which she had jotted down some things she thought I should know for her history, and I could see the paper trembling in her hand.

She wanted to find out several things: whether she had a physiological problem that was preventing conception; if so, whether the problem could be corrected; or whether it was Alex who was infertile. And like all infertility patients who are sincere in desiring children, she really wanted an answer. If it was, "No, you cannot have children," that would be better than the uncertainty. Then she could go home and get into bed and make love to make love, not as she and Alex had been doing—having intercourse to get pregnant. Then she wouldn't cry every month when she got her menstrual period. And Alex wouldn't call from work to find out whether it had come.

I had told Betsy to take a sample of Alex's sperm in any clean, dry container, like a mayonnaise jar, to a specialist in semen analysis. We learned that Alex didn't have a very high number of active sperm. The number of sperm isn't actually the critical factor. If you have 300 million sperm that are immobile—they're lying there wagging their tails, so to speak—you've got lots of sperm but you're not fertile. You're better off with 20 million actively mobile sperm. I told Betsy we could try artificial insemination using Alex's semen, but they decided to make another effort to have a baby themselves.

Half a year later, they were still unsuccessful, and Betsy came back to talk. The recent months had been difficult for them because they'd been making such a determined effort to get Betsy pregnant. During her fertile days, they wouldn't just have intercourse at night, but Alex would come home from the office at lunchtime or early in the afternoon. It had gotten so they couldn't go to bed to make love. They were always thinking about conception. During that visit, Betsy asked me about the artificial-insemination-husband, which we call AIH. She wanted to know whether we would really be using Alex's sperm.

I said yes.

She said she didn't understand why artificial insemination would work any better than natural means if we were using the same semen.

So I explained that the vagina is a pretty big organ when you talk in terms of surface area. During intercourse, when it's stretched and converted into a tube, there is a large area over which the man's teaspoonful of ejaculate, or semen, sprays, and actually you're lucky that any gets to the cervix. What we do is take that teaspoonful of stuff and put it into a little plastic cup or cap which we insert right up against the cervix, so the sperm can't go anywhere else. It only takes a minute to do. It's exactly like putting in a diaphragm. As a matter of fact, you could use a diaphragm except that it is impregnated with spermicidal, or sperm-killing, material.

Betsy said, "So you won't be mixing anybody else's sperm with Alex's."

"Absolutely not," I said. "You and Alex would have to sign legal papers before I could use a donor's specimen."

She agreed then and there to try AIH. We figured out approximately when she would ovulate next, and I told her she would have to bring in a specimen of Alex's sperm two or three times during her fertile period. I explained she would probably be inseminated in the morning, leave the cervical cap in during the day, and take it out that night. It's got a little string attached to it, and you pull on the string. Occasionally the cap sucks up against the cervix, and you have to reach in and break the suction, but then it just pulls right out.

Well, I'd been trying to get Betsy pregnant this way for three months. One morning she canceled an appointment because Alex hadn't been able to get a specimen, so I guess they were becoming more and more nervous. But that day he came home from the office to give her a specimen and we saw her late in the afternoon. I put the cap in and told her to leave it there overnight. She always thanked me after I did this, and that evening she added, "You know, Dr. Sweeney, I really don't mind having the cap in. The whole time it's there, I feel very close to Alex."

So now, about two weeks later, I picked up my office phone and Betsy was on.

"Hi, Betsy, how are you?"

"Oh, I'm so glad you can talk to me, Dr. Sweeney."

She sounded absolutely bubbly.

"What's the excitement?"

"I've been waiting three days to call you and I couldn't wait another minute," she said. "It's my temperature: it's still up. It should have dropped three days ago, and I should have gotten my period by now. I'm late and there's no staining." She hesitated. "Do you think this time it worked?"

I could picture her brown curls bouncing and her brown eyes all excited. She was a shiny sort of girl when she was happy, which hadn't been often in my office.

"It sounds good, Betsy, but it's a little too early to tell. Will you call me in a couple of days and let me know what's happening?"

She got the message. It was hard for me to cut into that bubble of happiness, but I didn't think she should get her hopes up too high when it was perfectly possible that she was just a few days late, that her temperature would fall and she'd still have her period.

"Sure, Dr. Sweeney, I'll call you." Her voice was subdued. "I know what you mean. We won't count on anything." Then the voice came back a little excited again. "But —I know this sounds silly, but I really feel pregnant. This time I feel different, and that's never happened before."

"Well, you won't catch me knocking woman's intuition," I told her. "But remember, I'll expect to hear from you in a couple of days."

And I hoped I wouldn't hear from her right away, because if she called soon it would be to say her temperature was down. And I loved this little girl. I wanted her and Alex to have a baby.

I sometimes don't see how anybody gets pregnant during an infertility workup because we have to take such a mechanical approach to an emotionally charged situation. Of course not everybody who asks for help really wants us to succeed. Some couples are playing games. They go home for a holiday and their parents or friends ask, "Why don't you have any children?" So they think about that. Maybe they haven't been using a contraceptive. Consciously or subconsciously, this lady and her husband may not want kids, but to save face, she'll come in with their "infertility problem." It doesn't take long, though, to know whether somebody really wants to have a baby. I may just ask, "Why do you want to become pregnant?" And I can pick out the ones who are here with their pat little answers: "It won't fulfill my femininity unless I have a baby." What the hell, that's no answer, it's something she read in the last issue of *Redbook*. Or the other bit, "My father and mother are getting old and it would give them so much happiness. . . ." Baloney. The answer to, "Why do you want to become pregnant?" most times out of ten from someone who really wants a kid is, "Because I like babies!"

Sometimes we spot the phonies in other ways. For example, a woman is supposed to keep a chart of her temperature every morning so we can see if and when she is ovulating. She has to take it immediately upon awaking, before arising, because her routine activity will drive it up to the accepted norm of 98.6. During ovulation, the waking temperature goes up from about 97.2 or .4 to about 98.2 or .4. Occasionally a patient brings in a chart we call bus temperatures. She didn't take them at all; she just put down the dots while she sat on the bus coming to my office. She may think she knows what a temperature chart should look like, but actually it doesn't look at all the way her women's magazine described. So when she comes in with her perfect little dots, I know.

On the other hand, it's not always the wife who is the uncooperative partner. All we ask from an infertility husband is a specimen of his sperm or semen. Now in a way that's asking a lot. The wife has to go home and tell him, "Dr. Sweeney wants you to masturbate into a bottle."

"Jesus Christ, that's what your fancy doctor told you to tell me!"

Some husbands say they can't do it, but they can all do it eventually. The man who can't just doesn't want his wife to be pregnant. I mean, this guy has probably been secretly masturbating since he was a little boy, and suddenly he can't, or it's against his principles? Bull.

I have even had husbands who will fake orgasms. In the middle of the wife's menstrual cycle when he figures she's going to be fertile, he just doesn't deposit any sperm. Some women protest, "I would know if that's what he was doing, wouldn't I? How unobservant do you think a woman is?" But there's only a teaspoonful of semen in the average adult man. When a lady gets out of bed and it runs from her vagina, it probably feels like four gallons, but it's not. And what about the guy who's only got half a teaspoon? His wife never has much running out, and he can fool her if he wants to.

Actually, despite all we know about conception, there's a great deal of witchcraft involved with infertility. Some people prefer to call it psychology, but that doesn't mean we understand the forces at work. Infertility doctors swap patients. For example, if I've done everything I can for a woman who has no physiological reason for not conceiving, I'll send her to somebody else. And I'll get patients in the same way. It's amazing the number of them who get pregnant when they switch. I've had infertility patients referred by another doctor, who *came in to me* already pregnant. Of course then I laughingly call up the referring doctor and take credit for the pregnancy. I suppose everyone knows at least one couple who finally gave up and adopted a child, and next thing they knew, the wife was pregnant.

There's a civilization in the Pacific where custom dictates that until the young girls marry, they sleep with all the men in the tribe. Then, after a girl chooses a husband, she's faithful to him. What's baffling is that none of these girls gets pregnant until she marries. As far as any investigation has been able to determine, these people aren't taking any mysterious herbs and they don't have their own secret contraceptive drugs. Yet the unmarried girls never get pregnant. I've seen cases where apparently similar psychological defenses were set up.

I remember one woman who came to Infertility Clinic, went through all the tests and then one day came in pregnant. Of course this was a big day for the Infertility Clinic; we felt pretty elated. But this woman sat down and cried. "I want an abortion." We talked and the story came out. She and her husband had always had intercourse without any protection and although they were both physically all right, she had never conceived. Then one night they returned from a party, both having had a lot to drink. She said goodnight to her husband and went to bed, but as she was falling asleep, he came to her, and before she knew what was happening, he was having intercourse with her. Presumably she didn't have time to set up whatever psychological barriers she normally erected, and she got pregnant. I don't know whether or not she went through with the abortion, because of course she never returned to Infertility Clinic.

So not every patient who claims she wants to be pregnant means it. But those who really want a baby will do anything in the world to conceive. I remember another lady who came to the clinic. At most other kinds of clinics there are no scheduled appointments, and sometimes the patient may even have to come back the next day. But Infertility Clinic works a little differently: appointments are given because there are certain tests we have to do at specific times of the day or month. One is called a p.c. or postcoital test: the woman has intercourse and then comes in immediately so we can take some mucus from her cervix and see how many active sperm are there. When this particular woman came in on a broiling August afternoon her skin was cold to the touch. We couldn't understand it until we talked to her and found out that her husband was a butcher, and the only way she could come in for her p.c. test at 1:30 P.M. was by going down to his butcher shop where they went back to the deep freeze and had intercourse on the butcher's block. She then came straight to clinic still cold from making love in the deep freeze. But there was no fuss about it because she wanted a baby that much.

I think those women who go to Infertility Clinic are in some ways the most courageous people I know. I always tell the medical students that the clinic patient with a gynecological or obstetrical problem is very special. She probably doesn't have enough money to go to a private doctor, but she's no less sensitive about intimate things than anyone else. So she comes to the great hospital and she expects a gray-haired kindly old doctor who's going to see her. What happens? First she's herded into a waiting room filled with other women and moved around. Finally, when it's her turn to have her history taken, who comes in but this bright-eyed, bushy-tailed little medical student. Now that's her first real contact with the hospital and she's shocked. I mean, she expected a distinguished fifty-year-old man and she got what she thinks is a twelve-year-old boy asking her when she last made love. I don't know how she answers any of the questions. Especially if this idiot sits down and says, "Okay, now let's go to work, when did you last have intercourse?" Or, "When was your last menstrual period?"

I think if I were that woman I'd either get up and leave, or I'd slap his little face or spank his behind. But if she can stomach the young doctor's unintentional crudeness, she's whisked into a small room and told to get undressed. Then she's put in the most ungodly position in the world with her legs spread wide apart, and in bounces this same little boy, accompanied by a nurse who looks like she's twelve and a half and never had a period in her life. Together they futz around and then they probably say, "Well, now we're going to have the older doctor examine you." And who walks in? A resident doctor, age thirty, or a young attending, age forty, both with hair down around their shoulders. She still hasn't got the gray-haired kindly old doctor she was looking for.

So clinics are difficult for patients, even though technically a woman probably gets the best medical care in the world at the clinic of a good teaching hospital. After the intern or resident examines her, she will be seen by as many senior men as necessary until her problem is solved. In many ways this lady is getting better medical care for free than a private patient who might be paying exorbitant fees to a doctor who may not be the best in the world and who probably won't consult anyone else for an evaluation.

But scientific care and knowledge aren't all a patient needs. There's an art to medicine that the young clinic doctors are lacking. The intern or resident is taught what questions to ask, but not how to ask them. He doesn't have to sit down and say, "Okay, now let's go to work. . . ." He can talk a little bit first. "How are things? Is it still raining?" Anything to break the ice. Or, especially in a crowded clinic, "There are some things we have to know in order to take care of you, but I'm sure we can keep our voices down so everybody doesn't have to hear us."

I can remember one resident at Infertility Clinic saying, "Now *I* want you to have intercourse at 2 P.M. and then come straight in here by two forty-five. . . ." After the woman left, I said, "What do you mean, *you* want her to do this and that? Don't you agree it sounds nicer to say, 'If it is possible for you to have intercourse at two, could you be here about two forty-five?' "

But none of this stops the woman who really wants to get pregnant. She'll willingly go through all the tests we make before we get around to the p.c. test. The only thing we need from her husband is one or maybe two samples of his semen, but we have to find out a lot more about this woman because she's much more complex than he is to start with.

Usually we begin by testing the thyroid. If this is normal, and if her temperatures indicate she's ovulating, we have to find out whether her fallopian tubes are open so the egg can pass through them. We generally do this by means of a Rubin test or tubal insufflation—"blowing the tubes" as the women call it. We insert an instrument that looks like a blunt syringe through the opening into the lady's cervix. Then we attach this syringe via a rubber tube to a tank of carbon dioxide, and we instill the gas into the uterus. As the pressure in the uterus increases, an indicator on a special machine records it on a piece of graph paper. If the tubes are not open, the indicator ascends to a point showing a pressure of 200 millimeters of mercury. The CO_2 then automatically cuts off and no more is instilled. If the tubes are open, the carbon dioxide can escape through them into the abdomen. When it does, the indicator falls rapidly as the pressure in the uterus drops. With a stethoscope you can hear the gas as it passes through the tubes.

The patient is awake while this test is going on, and it's not very pleasant for her to have this thing stuck up into her uterus in the first place. If the tubes are blocked, the gas hurts. If they're open and the gas goes through, when this woman stands up she gets a tremendous sharp pain in her shoulder because her tummy is full of CO_2 and the pressure affects a nerve in her diaphragm which branches upward.

The Rubin test is really pretty unrefined. A better method is to inject some radio-opaque material through the uterus and take X-rays as it fills the tubes and does or doesn't spill into the abdomen. Unfortunately this "hysterosalpingogram" or hystogram, for short, is expensive and time-consuming. More important, I am conservative about doing it because it exposes the ovaries and eggs to radiation.

Once we're ready to do the postcoital test, these women have to go home and have intercourse that is not love-making. It's just plain, "Lie down and have intercourse on the twelfth, fourteenth and sixteenth days, dear, because Dr. Sweeney says we have to."

And a lot of husbands really can't do that. I always tell my ladies to go home and use their feminine wiles. "Don't ever say, 'We have to do such and such for Dr. Sweeney.' You can con him." So it's the twelfth, fourteenth and sixteenth and he doesn't know what's happening; he's having intercourse but he's making love. The wife is just having intercourse because she's thinking about the dates and the reason, but he can be had. There's more to fertility than screwing, let's face it.

If a wife has a husband with no sperm and she wants to get pregnant, either she has an affair or she asks for artificial in-

semination with a male donor. That first alternative probably
seems shocking. Certainly if the husband knows he has no
sperm, it presents a problem. But if you're in my business
for a while, you run into stories you really have trouble
believing.

I know of a family in Atlanta, Georgia, which sat down
as a group and concluded that since one brother couldn't get
his wife Nancy pregnant, the other brother should. And they
not only wanted the brother to get her pregnant but decided
he should do it by having intercourse with her. Nancy was
a former patient of mine, and one day while she was in New
York visiting her parents, she came to see me. She didn't
really want the routine examination, although that's what
she made the appointment for. But when she reached my
office, she just started crying and out came the story of this
incredible clan in Atlanta and this husband who wouldn't
accept insemination from anybody but his brother because
he felt no other family was good enough.

I said, "Nancy, you're out of your mind. Don't you *dare*
do this."

Just think what the emotional situation would be—not to
mention the legal ramifications of their knowing who the
real father was. What would happen if she ever split up with
this husband of hers and he didn't want to support the baby?
All he had to do was say, "It's not my baby." His wife would
have committed adultery. And he'd have the witnesses to
prove it. Nancy finally got a divorce from that crazy man,
and she came in about a year later—she had moved back to
New York—looking very happy, freed of many problems.

I had another girl visit the office quite recently. She was
single, the daughter of a college dean in New England. She
asked if I did artificial insemination.

I said yes, we did.

She asked, "With donors?"

I said yes, we did AID.

"Well, I want one," she said.

"But you're not married."

"What do you care whether or not I'm married?"

"What about your parents?" I asked.

"I told them I wanted to have a child."

The next obvious question was, "If you want a child this much, why don't you get one the normal way? If that's what you're sure you want, go get pregnant."

She had tried that and it didn't work, so now she wanted AID.

Well, that's a pretty tough nut. What do I do with that one? Usually when they're married, I think, "How good a home will the baby have?" This was a really strange girl, and I finally said we couldn't do it. Yet to be honest, I don't know why we couldn't. One of my problems was, when we use a donor, the husband signs permission, not only to allow us to do the insemination, but to acknowledge he knows it's AID. It's easy for a woman to say, "I don't have to have that written thing. My husband loves me more than anything in the world and he wants me to have a baby." But who knows, five years later, maybe he calls the baby a bastard, it's not his, they don't know who the father is, and they're getting divorced. Well, *is* that a bastard child? The woman hasn't actually committed adultery because she hasn't had intercourse with someone other than her lawful spouse. But there has been at least one court ruling that said a child born as the result of AID was a bastard.

So here was this single girl, nobody to sign permission, and she was asking me to inseminate her with a donor specimen. How could I be sure that she wasn't going to come back two years later and say, "Look what this guy did to me: *he* got me pregnant." I wouldn't have a leg to stand on. I could have asked her for a written statement that she had requested AID, but it wouldn't hold up in court; it's easy enough to claim something was written under duress. I suppose I could have gotten written permission from her parents, although they were no longer her legal guardians since she was over twenty-one.

She was angry that I wouldn't do the insemination, and she had a point. "What business is it of yours if I'm married or not?" she asked.

And it wasn't any of my business. If she wanted a baby, I suppose she was entitled to have one. Certainly there's no law that says you have to be married, or even female, to *adopt* a child. But I said no.

One of my problems is what to say to a man who has no sperm. This is a terrible blow to him. As a matter of fact, I never tell anybody he hasn't got any sperm. Even if his count is zero, I just say it's very low.

I saw a woman the other day whose husband had been married before. When his first wife left him, he became impotent. Then he fell in love with this woman and got back to the point where he could have sexual relations. But he's sterile, and they've been trying to get pregnant. What am I going to do? He'll probably become impotent again if I tell him he has no sperm. I'm not going to destroy both this marriage and this man by telling him he's zero. I'm going to say his count is very low; then I'll get permission to do AID and ask for his specimen to mix with the donor's. Now what have we lost? Suppose this guy *has* two or four million sperm. Who knows, is it his sperm or the other guy's that made the woman pregnant? AID is just a little easier to accept if you don't know positively.

It's a hell of a decision for a man to make—that he's going to allow his wife to be impregnated by another man's sperm. Even though she hasn't been out screwing, she's pregnant by somebody else. And it's tough on her. When we're doing artificial-insemination-donor, there's a silence in the examination room you could cut with a knife. Something bad is happening. In some way, she's cheating on her husband. And we hardly ever have it take the first month. Her whole body rejects it. It may work the second month, or the third, but not the first.

We usually get donors from the hospitals—the young doctors and medical students. Back when I was a resident, if you offered people $15 or $25 for a specimen of their semen, which meant they had to run up and masturbate before they went to the operating room to work, well, $15 was a lot of money, and we had no problem getting donors. Now, the residents don't care about the lousy $15. It's awful to have to say to a couple who has finally reached the point where they can accept AID, "I'm sorry, I have no donors."

The donor shortage may eventually be alleviated through the use of frozen sperm banks. Human sperm can be frozen and such banks do exist. In principle I think they are an excellent and exciting advance. But at this time, I agree with the organizations that feel the controls on donors right now are insufficient. Therefore I don't use sperm banks as a source of AID semen.

Not everybody can be a donor. While I guess there's no law against it, we wouldn't want to take donors from a prison. Certainly there are health qualifications; and most of the people who would be used in a university or teaching hospital have a better than average intelligence. Equally important, we like to use men who have proven their fertility, either by having children or by having their sperm evaluated. Of course, this kind of careful selection and testing leads to a couple of other problems. You end up limiting the number of donors in your stable because you just don't have time to check all the potentially qualified people. But you can't let one man be the father of too many babies, either!

Some people come in and lay down their donor specifica-

tions—"I only want a Jewish donor," or, "I don't want a
Jewish donor." But the majority leave the selection up to us.
What we do is try to match the mother or the couple, without knowing specifically who the donor is. We call up and
say we've got a dark-haired five-foot-three Jewish girl, or a
five-foot-ten Scandinavian girl, and we would like a similar
partner. The results are sometimes surprising.

I have one patient—I love her dearly—who's a black-
haired, black-eyed really sweet little girl. I inseminated her
with a donor specimen mixed with her husband's although he
was practically zero. She got pregnant, and she stayed with
me. A lot of women don't want to keep the same obstetrician
if they conceive by AID. I know about the AID; the secretary knows because she has to call up for the donor specimen
and coordinate things—you can only keep sperm for a couple
of hours after it's donated—and of course the nurse who
works with me knows what I'm doing. Many many times,
when that woman gets pregnant, she wants to walk into
another obstetrician's office and say it's her husband's baby
and feel more like everybody else. But when this little girl
got pregnant, she didn't want to switch doctors. She was petri-
fied, of course—everybody is—that there was going to be
something wrong with the baby, but the baby was a healthy
little boy. No one outside of my office knew he was an artificially inseminated child. I saw the mother postpartum, or
after delivery, for a couple of days, and she was very happy.
Then one day I walked in and she was absolutely *radiant*.

"What's happened that's got you glowing like that?" I
asked.

"Jerry's aunt came in today and she said, 'The baby looks
just like Jerry did when *he* was a little boy!' "

That's always the greatest joy for AID parents, and you'd
be amazed how many of the kids look like the husband.
I've done two inseminations for the same lady with two dif-

ferent donors and the kids have come out looking alike. I fathered three boys and they don't look alike at all. So who knows all the elements that are working in this thing? And as long as the baby is healthy and the parents are happy, who cares?

9. Menopause and Myths

Agnes Skrapits didn't want to sit down. She stood facing my desk, a strongly built woman of medium height wearing a white uniform which buttoned tightly across her ample bosom.

Mrs. Skrapits had been referred to me by Charlotte Widener, a patient of mine for whom Agnes worked as a cleaning woman. When Mrs. Widener made the appointment she told me Agnes hadn't been feeling well.

"It's been going on for weeks," Charlotte said. "Agnes is forty-eight. She's a dignified lady. I can't just ask her if she's having her menopause, but that's what it looks like to me. Anyway, she doesn't have a gynecologist so I thought she should see you."

I looked at Mrs. Skrapits's chart. In the examining room she had told me her menstrual periods had been irregular for some time. She had had none for three months.

I asked Mrs. Skrapits if she understood what menopause was. She appeared uncertain, but when I said "change of life," she nodded vigorously.

"I have it now." She spoke with a Hungarian accent. At first she had thought she was coming down with the flu, but then she realized what her symptoms meant. She told me she had two grown children and it was time for her change.

"I have no trouble except too much sweat," she said. She explained that sometimes she became hot and perspired at work even though she might be sitting quietly polishing silver.

I asked her how often it happened.

"Maybe two, three times a day," she answered. "It comes more now, I think."

"What about at night?"

Mrs. Skrapits looked past my shoulder. "Night is not good anymore," she said. "Not good for sleep." Suddenly, in a rush of words, she described the hot flushes that caused her to wake up soaking wet. She had to get out of bed and change her nightgown and maybe the pillowcase or sheet. By the time she got back into bed, she was cold. Then just as she was falling asleep again, she would have another one of these things, so she might be up for hours.

"Last night I feel hot and open all the windows," Agnes said. "My Yoshka—my husband Joe—says he is freezing. He asks me am I crazy?" Her glance remained fixed on the point beyond my shoulder. "I am not crazy. I think all women have this. But when he says that to me I feel . . ." She was unable to find the expression. Mentally I filled in the word another woman had used: humiliated.

"Mrs. Skrapits, we can give you some pills that will make you feel better," I said.

"I am not sick," she corrected me. "Only too much sweat." Suddenly her fair skin flushed deep pink and perspiration broke out on her forehead and upper lip. Women who suffer these terrific flushes become red and perspired because of a sudden dilating of the veins. The veins trap the blood in the area of the flushed zone. It's the same process as a blush. Mrs. Skrapits pulled a handkerchief from her purse and rubbed it across her face.

"I don't feel sorry for this to happen in front of you," she said. "You are a doctor. But if we have tea with friends . . ." Her voice trailed off. "I tell myself, 'Agnes, you are not so beautiful that everyone is watching you.' But someone I am talking to is looking. And Yoshka sees."

"Mrs. Skrapits, I can give you pills to stop the sweating," I said. "You won't get hot and then cold. And you'll sleep through the night."

"That would be wonderful. I like to go to work and feel good. I like to be with friends and look like everyone else."

I wrote a prescription for 0.625 milligrams of Premarin, a synthetic estrogen. I told Mrs. Skrapits to take one pill every morning for the first three weeks of each month and no pills during the last week of the month. Finally I made sure she understood that she might have some bleeding during the week she was not taking the pills, and that was all right. But if she had bleeding at any other time, she was to call me.

One of the real dangers of estrogens is that a woman taking them may assume the hormones are causing bleeding, when actually she might have grown a cancer inside her uterus that's causing it to bleed. And when she finally comes for a visit, she's got an advanced malignancy—not because the estrogens grew it, but because she ignored the symptom of bleeding.

Mrs. Skrapits left, promising to return for an examination in six months. Her prescription would run out then, so I knew she wouldn't be taking the hormones without supervision.

Two months later when Charlotte Widener came in for a checkup, I got an immediate report on Mrs. Skrapits.

"Agnes feels wonderful," Charlotte said. "She says you gave her magic pills."

I smiled. "I wish you'd let me take them away from you."

"Why should I give them up when I feel this good?" Charlotte asked.

"Because you don't need Premarin. You never did. I told you that from the first."

Charlotte Widener had stopped menstruating four years earlier, at the age of fifty-two. She had come to see me after three months of no periods, furious at having reached menopause and distraught because, as she put it, "There was no warning. I was always regular as clockwork. Then it stopped, just like that."

I had tried to convince her that in some ways it would be nice if everyone stopped suddenly. Maybe not so nice psychologically, because women need time to get used to the idea. But the woman who becomes irregular and stops gradually is the one who has a menopausal baby. She doesn't get her period for a couple of months, tosses the diaphragm out and then turns up pregnant in middle age.

I had warned Charlotte not to have intercourse without protection for at least six months. Then one day she called to say I had been right and she was having a period. She sounded quite pleased, which was far from how I felt about the news.

As doctors, we have to assign some length of time beyond

which we say that any bleeding is abnormal. I select six months as my time limit. If a woman has bleeding after six months of no periods, then in my book this is postmenopausal bleeding. Anybody who has postmenopausal bleeding has cancer of the uterus until we rule it out, and I admit every single one of them to the hospital and do a dilatation and curettage. I don't care if it's negative; if six months later she bleeds again, she gets another D and C. But what about the woman who goes *five* months and then bleeds? Is it a "normal" period? She hasn't quite reached my classification of postmenopausal bleeding, so I'm not taking her to the hospital for a D and C. But maybe she's got a cancer. And we worry about her. This is the main reason it would be better from a medical point of view if everybody stopped menstruating suddenly.

According to Charlotte's chart, her "period" was right at the six-month time limit. I told her I wanted to do a dilatation and curettage. Her initial objections disappeared when I explained my reasons. Fortunately her D and C was negative, and she didn't bleed again. She also had none of the symptoms some women get with menopause, although she'd been watching for them. But one visit after I had done the D and C, she said, "Dr. Sweeney, I want to take some hormones for my menopause."

"Why?"

"I think they'll make me feel better."

"How do you feel now?"

"Fine, I guess."

"Then I don't understand."

Certainly in this day and age I don't think anybody with a normal medical history should be saddled with menopausal symptoms. Besides hot flushes and chills, some women get depressed. The emotion can vary from a relatively mild case of testiness or bitchiness toward husband and friends to severe depression, in which the woman is sad and cries and sits around feeling unattractive, not wanting to go anywhere or do anything. Headaches, insomnia and a sense of anxiety can also occur.

The cause of these symptoms is lack of estrogen. We assume this is true because if we give a lady estrogens by mouth or injection, replacing these hormones her ovaries stop making after menopause, her symptoms are relieved. But Charlotte had no symptoms.

"Suppose I begin flushing," she said.

"We'll give you estrogens then. But most women do not have any menopausal symptoms. And you're a case in point."

Charlotte looked undecided. "Most of my friends are taking Premarin. I understand it can do some very good things," she added vaguely.

Charlotte Widener is not a vague woman. "What good things?" I asked.

"Well, for your skin," she said.

"They might make your skin or hair a little less dry, but it's a fractional difference. I bet if you took ten women who were sixty-five years old, five on estrogens and five not, only a plastic surgeon could look at their skin and see some difference."

"What about taking estrogens for . . . your sex life?"

"Go on," I said.

Charlotte took a paperback volume from her purse. "May I read you something?" she asked.

"Sure. What's the book?"

She held it up. It was Dr. Reuben's *Everything You Always Wanted to Know About Sex But Were Afraid to Ask.* She opened to a place mark and started reading. If my hair weren't already gray, it would have silvered while I listened to some of the things Dr. Reuben had written about menopause.

First of all, he made it sound as though all women got menopausal symptoms, which I flatly told Charlotte was not true. "If a hundred menopausal ladies came in here right now, probably seventy to eighty of them would have no symptoms at all. It's just that those who do talk so much about them, you get the impression that everybody in the world has flushes and flashes and all the rest."

Charlotte went on quoting. "Estrogen rules women sexually," Dr. Reuben wrote, adding, "It is the ebb and flow of estrogenic hormone during the menstrual cycle that is primarily responsible for the variations in female sexual desire. Once the ovaries stop, the very essence of being a woman stops."

"That's ridiculous," I said. "Dr. Reuben is a psychiatrist, and maybe that's how it looks from behind the couch if his patients are having psychological problems adjusting to menopause. But you do not need estrogen to want sex. If you've always liked it and it's been fun, you'll keep on wanting it. Maybe some women who never really enjoyed sex are glad to have menopause as an excuse for ending that activity. Usually, if you want to tell the honest-to-God truth, when a woman's interest in sex diminishes, it's probably because the husband can't get an erection and maintain it, so they don't have intercourse. I've had women who went through menopause without taking any hormones whose major complaint was that they wanted more sex than they were getting. I've got a little girl in her late twenties whose ovaries were removed two years ago, and for medical reasons we're not giving her hormones. There's nothing sexier in this world than she is. I'd like to bring her in here and read that guy's thing to her. She'd kill him!"

The next thing Mrs. Widener read me was about changes in the vagina. At one point I interrupted, "What's that about her vagina shrinking?"

She read it again: "Patient questioning by the doctor re-
vealed Irene was trying to tell him her vagina was shrinking.
The atrophy had progressed to the point where the vaginal
opening would no longer admit her husband's penis."

"Oh, my God, that's just baloney," I said. "The vagina
would shrink only if it wasn't being used. Changes do take
place in the lining of the vagina as you get older, just as
changes take place in your skin. There may not be as much
lubrication, so intercourse may become more difficult. And
some women get what's called senile vaginitis. But in cases
like those, I think a local estrogenic cream is preferable to
pills that affect the whole system. In any event, the vagina
doesn't begin to shrivel or shrink."

"Do the breasts change?" Charlotte asked.

"They get a little smaller, and so does the uterus. But I
don't think anyone knows whether that's because of menopause per se, or whether it's a question of aging. Little old
ladies are little partly because there is a general loss of fatty
tissue and elasticity throughout the body. However, old men
are smaller too, and they're not suffering from estrogen lack."

Charlotte resumed reading a list of terrible menopausal
symptoms which included increased facial hair, a deeper
voice like a man's and coarsened features.

"No," I said. "A woman does not get those things because
of her change of life. Maybe back in the days when hormones
were in the experimental stage and some ladies were given
male hormones for too long or in too large a dose, these
masculine changes might have occurred. But a woman today
is not going to get these symptoms with menopause unless
she is the rare exception or unless she has a pituitary tumor.
If a woman is going to have facial hair, it usually appears before menopause, and estrogens won't get rid of it. Only elec-
trolysis will. As for vocal tone, Marlene Dietrich made a
fortune with a deep sexy voice and she didn't wait for meno-

pause to get it. In any case, all the estrogens in the world won't raise someone's voice an octave or two."

The next symptom Mrs. Widener described was enlargement of the clitoris. Now there's a good one. Christ almighty. It isn't true. What may happen is that the clitoris looks a tiny bit larger because the surrounding tissue has shrunk slightly, due to a decrease in the amount of fat in that area. But the clitoris is exactly the same.

Reading time was over and Charlotte knew pretty well what I thought of this stuff, but she said, "I don't understand what you have against hormones even if they only help a little."

"I've got nothing against them when there are signs of a deficiency. But when there are no symptoms, I don't think there's any valid reason to prescribe estrogens. After all, you do have breasts and a uterus, and estrogens will stimulate growth there."

"You're talking about cancer, aren't you?"

"I'm only saying that estrogens stimulate growth, which is why a woman's breasts may look a little better or not sag if she's taking hormones. When you stimulate growth, no one can predict what the results might be."

Charlotte told me she would think about what I had said.

Three months later she was back asking for Premarin again. "I guess it's hard for a man to understand," she said, "but if a woman thinks she can look or feel even a little younger, she just wants to."

So I gave her the Premarin. She's been taking it ever since and won't give it up because she believes it makes her feel better. I'm not sure I couldn't have accomplished the same thing with sugar pills, but we'll never know.

There's a big controversy, of course, about whether to give hormones. Some doctors put everybody on them, menopausal or not, because they feel hormones help keep people young.

But hormones won't change the fact that you're getting older, that there's no fountain of youth. Other doctors think nobody should take hormones. It's a shame for their patients that most gynecologists are men and most men do not have menopausal symptoms, so they don't realize how uncomfortable a woman can be. I obviously agree with those gynecologists who believe that people who are symptomatic, or show signs of estrogen lack such as flushes or depression, ought to be given some sort of hormone replacement. I also think that some older ladies who have demineralization of the bones may be helped with estrogens. And if we remove a young woman's ovaries, giving her a sudden, premature surgical menopause, we should replace her hormones during the years she would have produced them naturally.

Actually, even a woman with complete ovarian loss has not been totally deprived of hormones. Although the ovary is the only source of progesterone, other areas such as the adrenal glands make estrogenlike substances. No one knows why some women have menopausal symptoms while most do not, but it may be that the nonsymptomatic ladies are compensating better with estrogen production from other areas of their body.

There's certainly a lot of disagreement over the quantity of estrogens you should use. I think some doctors give an ungodly amount. There is no evidence that estrogens are going to cause cancer, but any product that's going to stimulate growth has to be used properly. That's why I believe that patients taking estrogens for menopause should be on the pills for three weeks and then off for one week. Such a cycle gives the lining of the uterus a chance to bleed if it's going to, although more often than not there is no "period." More important, it means that the breasts won't be constantly stimulated.

I also think certain women just shouldn't take estrogens.

Consider the lady who has had cancer of the breast and who is menopausal and symptomatic. Do we put her on estrogens when we know darn well they're going to stimulate the breasts? At that stage of the game, do we want to give her any medicine that will stimulate growth? How do we know what might tip things over from a stimulated change into a malignant change? We really don't know that much about the whole business.

Cancer is not something from without that moves in. Cancer is a normal growth that changes into a malignant growth. The breast tissue that becomes cancerous was normal at one time. Cancer simply involves a change in growth pattern. Normal growth entails cell proliferation, the breaking from one cell into two cells into four into eight and so forth. In a malignant process, the lesion, or structural change, doesn't play by the rules. The proliferation takes place, but two cells may go to fifteen instead of four; and in doing so, the cells themselves become abnormal. But we don't know what stimulus causes this change in growth pattern. That's why I'm conservative about prescribing hormones without valid indications.

A big problem I have to face, and I don't really know the answer, is how long should we permit somebody to continue on hormones. Until she's sixty? Seventy? Eighty? Usually with a woman who has had symptoms, I'll discontinue the estrogens after a year. Unless there are some difficulties, I'll keep her off. And most patients like Charlotte Widener eventually solve my problem for me. They get tired of taking those pills and stop.

Unfortunately hormones are like vitamins in one respect: lay people have demanded vitamins when they don't need them, and they have demanded hormones when they don't need them. This partly reflects our dream of staying young, but I think it also reflects fear. Women have been frightened by all kinds of stories and myths and misinformation about menopause. Some ladies are afraid of "going crazy" or losing their memory "at that time." They won't, unless they develop a rare condition called Alzheimer's disease, which affects the brain. But the rumors persist because people focus on the exceptions and ignore what is typical. Furthermore, any irregularity in behavior is apt to be blamed on the menopause. If a young woman forgets a dinner date, people shrug it off. Let an older woman do the same thing and everyone looks serious. "She's at that time of life, you know."

A lot of women hate the thought of having reached their so-called Change because they associate it with growing old. In a way, that's understandable. Menopause by definition is just a cessation of the menses, or menstrual flow. It can take place anytime after age thirty-five, although most women go through it between ages forty-five and fifty-five. Until recently, however, women did not live for long after their menopause. In the United States, a woman born at the turn of the century had an average life expectancy of 48.3 years. So by the standards of her time, she would indeed be "old" when she reached menopause. Today the average life expectancy of a woman is over seventy-three years. Yet the association of menopause with old age often remains.

In addition, some ladies face a tremendous psychological adjustment to the idea that they can no longer have children. An important stage of their lives has ended. On the other hand, a lot of women are relieved to know they can't become pregnant anymore. They can forget the diaphragm, or stop the withdrawal they both hate so much. Or the guy can throw away those condoms which are made by the Devil and Company.

The way a woman reacts emotionally to menopause depends largely, I believe, on her sense of identity as a person and on what she is taught to expect as a woman. I tell my patients that menopause is perfectly natural, that about 80 percent of women don't have any adverse symptoms, but that if they need estrogens, I'm not going to withhold them. I think the time will soon come when people will stop viewing menopause as a crisis.

10. Sandra Stevens

I always ask mothers who come to my office if they've brought any photos of their children. At first, lots of them think, "Aw, no, he doesn't really want to see pictures." But finally I convince them, and some come in with albums, or send photos at Christmas so I get to see the kids growing up. The other morning I got a little spiral notebook from the Simpsons. Jean had made it into a miniature album with a caption under each picture and a note from their baby:

Dear Dr. Sweeney:

I suppose I'm too young to really express my gratitude properly, but my parents don't seem able to do it any better. So thank you from the bottom of my heart for being there all that time and making it possible for me to get born.

Love,

William Edward Simpson

P.S. I hope you don't mind that they've taken the liberty of naming me after you.

This made me feel pretty good. Not just the idea that they

named their boy after me. That sometimes happens, although with a name like Bill, you don't know whether they're really naming it after you or not. I try to get some of these women to name their little girls Wilhelmina but they won't. Anyhow I always save keepsakes like this little book, and I love to open a chart and see pictures of kids I've delivered.

Sandra Stevens didn't have any photos, so she brought in some slides with a projector. We sat here and focused them on the wall and watched her two girls—Cathy, ten, and Wendy, four.

Sandra is an old friend, an artist. She's not especially pretty, but she has a good figure and moves gracefully. I enjoyed her pictures and narrative, but I wasn't feeling as good as I might have been, because in a way I was lying to Sandra about the reason she'd been coming in. She thought she just had an infection. Actually, her husband had given her a venereal disease, and I knew enough about this couple to be sure it would destroy their marriage if I told her the truth.

Ten years ago I delivered Sandra Stevens's first baby by hypnosis. I think this is a tremendously safe and effective way to deliver. A lot of people are skeptical about hypnotism in general, but there's nothing great about it. Hypnosis is just suggestion. The guy who does it professionally is an expert at getting subjects to relax and respond to his suggestions. But every mother in the world uses hypnosis. If her little baby falls down, she picks the baby up and says, "Let Mommy kiss it and make it better." Mommy kisses it and it's all better. That's hypnosis. Doctors use it every day. We're going to take some blood out of a lady's arm. We say, "This is just like a little bee sting." We don't say, "This is going to hurt like hell!" Then it would hurt like hell!

I've been hypnotized. I took a concentrated three-day course in hypnosis, and part of it was undergoing the experience yourself. It's a delightful way to feel. I think if the young kids found out about it, they'd say it was much more fun than tripping. It is a trip. You're off in a little world of your own. If somebody tells you you're lying in a hammock and it's warm, you feel warm and comfortable and pleasant.

Now, we're medical hypnotists; we're not playing games. My object in hypnosis is to take away somebody's pain, or make it acceptable or make the woman ignore it. If I've got a good patient—and some people can be hypnotized better than others—I can say, "Picture a movie screen." And she'll see the movie screen. "Now you'll see a lady in labor on the movie screen." And she'll see the lady in labor. It's actually herself that she's watching, and she can tell me just what's going on.

People have a lot of misconceptions about hypnosis. Not only is the subject highly aware and awake while she's lying there, but she can talk. She can stop the hypnosis anytime she wants. I've told her ahead of time, "If it hurts, tell me." And occasionally somebody will say, "That's enough; give me some medication." But it's amazing to watch when it works.

I remember one woman I delivered. Her husband was an anesthesiologist, and he was in the room. This guy was committed to anesthesia, and his wife, by her own choice, was under hypnosis. I delivered the baby with no problem. And there I was sewing away to close the episiotomy when this guy passed out cold in the corner while his wife lay there quietly, saying, "It doesn't hurt, go ahead."

Now the question is, is it working? Is she really hypnotized?

I don't care. I mean, labor hurts like hell, and if she's going to lie there and let me cut her with a great big pair of scissors and then sew her up and say it doesn't hurt just to fool me, she can go ahead and fool me. But it must work. Nobody's that crazy. You might be nuts enough to let me stick a little tiny needle in your hand and pretend not to feel it, or you might be willing to make yourself real stiff and be placed across two separated chairs, but you're not playing games in labor.

When I first started doing hypnosis, I kept checking my patient's trance. I'd say, "Your arm is dead, I'll stick a needle in it." Finally I figured out I was only checking myself. And it gets across to the patient that you're not quite sure; then she starts waking up. So after a while, you just make damn certain that they're under, and you don't lie to them and they don't lie to you.

One of the problems with using hypnosis for deliveries is that the obstetrician is the only person the hypnotized woman will listen to. The husband is worthless at this point. He just stands there like a bump on a log while I'm delivering his wife. And if one of the nurses tells her to do something, she just won't pay any attention. But I tell this hypnotized woman something and she'll do *exactly* what I say. So the hypnotist has to be careful with his instructions. Suppose, for example, I tell you as the reader, "Raise your right hand." If you'll really try this, you'll learn something interesting about hypnotism. Go ahead and raise your right hand. Okay, now think about what you did. You probably raised your right hand *and arm* from the elbow. A hypnotized patient would have moved only her hand, from the wrist. So a hypnotist has to be careful about what he says and what his patient's interpretation is going to be. Suppose I tell a lady lying on a delivery table, "Raise your hips." What I want her to do is raise her buttocks, but she'll lie there and try to raise her hips and she won't be able to get them off the table.

Another trouble with hypnosis is that it takes a great deal of time. I believe you have to prepare patients by hypnotizing them four or five times first. That's four or five solid hours before you even get to the delivery. So when my load of pregnancies got too big, I had to stop doing it; it just wasn't practical. In fact, Sandra Stevens was the last patient I delivered this way.

She was a good subject. To practice, I would put a blood-pressure cuff around her arm and blow it up until it hurt, and I'd say, "Now this is what a contraction feels like." I don't know firsthand if that's what it feels like, but that was as close as I could get. Then I'd unhook the cuff and whoosh, her arm would go rushing back to normal. Then I'd hypnotize her and blow it up again, hard, so she could see that in the trance the pain didn't bother her.

I was glad I could spend the time with Sandra because she got no support from her husband, Ted. Ted Stevens was a doctor—a researcher working with leukemia—and not only was he wrapped up in his work, but Sandra said he had cut her off emotionally, treating this whole affair of having a baby as if it were her project. She told me once that her husband didn't like to get involved with her "problems" if there was nothing he could do physically to help.

I guess maybe she wanted this baby more than her husband did. In any case, I never met Ted Stevens during the course of Sandra's pregnancy. When Sandra had the baby, Dr. Stevens was down in Washington, D.C., on business about research grants, and he didn't fly back until two days after their daughter was born. The delivery went smoothly enough, but shortly after Sandra went home, she developed a post-partum psychosis. Not just the blues, but a real psychosis, or mental disease, and she had to be admitted to Payne Whitney Psychiatric Clinic for three months.

Almost every mother gets the blues to a certain extent sometime after her baby is born. I warn my patients that it's going to happen so they won't be afraid if it hits. Some women just can't go through nine months of being pregnant, then finally have the baby and take it all in stride. All sorts of fears have been cooped up in there, perhaps unvoiced. The expectant mother may have had nightmares about delivering a defective child. And especially if it's her first baby, she's afraid of labor. She doesn't know what it's like or how she's going to act. Then she goes into labor and has the baby and everything's fine: it's a healthy baby, the husband loves her and their child, and the friends come to visit. Flowers and telegrams arrive. The baby is brought in to be fed and taken away, and the mother is free to enjoy her company or read or do whatever she wants. Right then there can be a letdown because the tension and worry and big event are over.

Or maybe she's just exhausted; that can cause depression. Childbirth is one hell of a lot of work. Anybody who labored at another job for seven or eight hours with no relief would sleep for a week, but this woman is up the next morning, maybe taking care of her baby.

Some mothers are fine until the minute they leave the hospital. Then a nurse hands this woman her baby and says, "Here it is, it's yours." And suddenly that full responsibility hits her. "It's my baby. I'm in charge of this child's whole life, and I'm tied to it." She may burst out crying on the spot.

Or the blues may hit when she gets home. Before she goes, I tell her, "This is your baby and it's your husband's baby also. But you were husband and wife long before you were mother and father. You can take the baby home and plunk it in the middle of the living room and revolve around it as if it's the only thing in the world, or you can take the baby home to join the family. If you used to go bowling once a week, go bowling but take the kid now." Otherwise the baby destroys the marriage, because from the time he's brought home, the couple don't talk to one another. Then, when the child's grown up, this man and woman find they have nothing left in common.

I also warn mothers, "You've been top banana as wife for two or three years. But don't be worried if suddenly your husband comes home and turns to his son instead of you. It's going to be hard. You've been there all day long taking care of this goddamned screaming kid, and he comes home and goes to it first, and that's a letdown. He doesn't love you any less for what you went through. He loves you more. But he's got a kid now. That's the way we dumb men are."

Most important, I say, "It's all right to be jealous of the baby." What happens is, this woman is jealous and she thinks, "Oh my God, what an awful mother I am."

I tell her, "I realize this is the most advanced child in our whole nursery, but unfortunately all it can do is eat, sleep, cry and soil itself. You take it home and change it and it cries, and you burp it and it cries, and you make sure the pins aren't sticking in it and it cries. It's two o'clock in the morning and by this time you could drop-kick it into the East River!" Of course on top of everything New Yorkers are always afraid the child is going to wake up the neighbors or somebody's going to knock on the door. "The point is, it's *all right* to sometimes hate this little bundle. There's a fine line between love and hate anyway. Just realize your feelings are perfectly normal."

Otherwise, there's the psychosis. The mother hates the baby and feels guilty. Or she's so fearful and anxious she can't face the whole thing.

When Sandra went home, she got none of the help or support she needed from Ted. At first I didn't know how serious it was. The day after she left the hospital, she called my office. She was crying, but when I asked what was the matter, she said, "Nothing."

"Sandra, something must be bothering you a lot. Why don't you tell me what it is?"

"I just called Ted at the hospital," she sobbed.

"What happened?"

"I wanted to talk to him about Cathy."

"What about Cathy?"

She cried for a minute and then said, "He said he was busy and 'What's the matter? Didn't you want to be a mother?' " Suddenly she stopped crying. "I'm sorry I bothered you, Dr. Sweeney." And she hung up.

This conversation stayed in my mind until I finally asked Katey to get Sandra on the phone. We tried for a couple of days but there was no answer until one evening I called late, just before leaving the hospital after night rounds. Dr. Stevens answered. He told me the baby was in the hands of a nurse at his sister's house. He had come home the night Sandra called me and found her sitting in her bathrobe in the bedroom while the baby was screaming in the nursery. When he asked Sandra what was wrong, she said, "I'm waiting for Mommy to come home. She has to feed me and I'm hungry."

Sandra's mother died when Sandra was six, so this remark indicated real trouble. Sandra was in a psychotic state. She was unable to face anything and had done what she could to escape. A little later, she became violent. Ted called a doctor friend and together they got her into Payne Whitney Psychiatric Clinic.

She was there for thirteen weeks, with absolutely no visitors allowed during the first six weeks. They've got comfortable accommodations in Payne Whitney, sort of like a college room if you lived alone. But the doors are heavy wood and they're locked at night.

I told the psychiatrist who was treating Sandra I thought someone should examine her since she had just had a baby. He said arrangements had already been made within the hospital; he felt it would be better if a doctor she didn't associate with the trauma examined her. At that point, Sandra didn't remember she had borne a child. She was twenty-two years old.

I saw Sandra subsequently as a gynecological patient. She went to a psychiatrist for more than two years, and things seemed to improve. She got a nurse for Cathy and went back to work as a commercial artist.

Six years passed after Cathy's birth, and I didn't think the Stevenses were considering having another baby. Then one day Sandra came in pregnant. She told me there'd been lots of ups and downs in her relationship with Ted. They had discussed divorce more than once, and Ted had said he was all for it except he couldn't afford it. It must be incredibly demoralizing for a woman to know her husband feels this way. During their better moments, Ted would say he wanted a second child, but Sandra was afraid to have another baby because their emotional situation was so insecure. Then their relationship improved for quite a while. She and Ted went to Bermuda for a vacation. Sandra told me, "It was the first real vacation we'd had together in years. I painted and had the ocean and sun and sand, and I felt good. I guess we both really unwound. We made love, and I decided not to use my diaphragm. It was sort of fatalistic. I didn't really expect to get pregnant, but I guess that's when I conceived."

Sandra's mood during her pregnancy was good. She said even Ted seemed excited about the coming event. And she made plans to have natural childbirth although Ted wouldn't attend the classes with her. "He *is* a doctor," she said, "and I think he'll change his mind and be there when the time comes."

Ted was at a conference in Chicago when Sandra went into labor and delivered. He flew back to New York the next day. Sandra said he seemed elated the first time he held his daughter, and he was attentive during her stay in the hospital. But about a week after she went home, I received a call from her.

"I don't know what happened, Dr. Sweeney," she said.

"Everything seemed fine, but now I've lost contact with Ted again. He doesn't want to hold Wendy, and we barely talk. It's as though the girls and I don't exist."

This was a heartbreaking situation, and a tough one, because what was I going to tell this woman? Go get a divorce? She needed her husband if he could just give her a little support. She wanted to keep the marriage going. I told her bluntly what I thought, and in a week or so, I got a long letter from her. It was written on a thick sheet of artist's paper, folded to fit in a standard envelope. The writing went fluidly across the page.

Dear Dr. Sweeney,

My first reaction after talking to you two days ago was, "Yes, I know Dr. Sweeney is right, but I forgot to tell him I still love this man in spite of everything." I guess I expected you to say I should tell Ted how much I needed him. But then I started analyzing our marriage.

Maybe I've needed Ted's approval and love too much. It's like my having Wendy by natural childbirth. I knew Ted was scornful of my low tolerance for pain, and that he would approve of this way of delivering. Then when it went so well, I was crushed that he wasn't there to see it. Imagine my seeking approval and love so desperately.

Wednesday night, fortified with two Manhattans and with your words in mind, I told him we had to talk. We did, for four hours. We went over eleven years of marriage and I was able to talk clearly and calmly, even though deep inside my feelings were in a turmoil. Ted actually praised the way I expressed myself. He thought I made many excellent points and was grateful for my scientific attitude. So you see, he respects the same lack of emotion he usually displays, whereas I am just the opposite. The only reason I could talk that way was that I felt so drained by the worry of the preceding days.

I told him almost exactly what you said: that he had to give me some emotional support and physical help from time to time

or I was going to ask him to leave, because I had to find someone who could give me and the girls at least the bare minimum
of what we need. And I said I would no longer accept money
as an obstacle. I even told him to consider whether his life
would be better if he were living alone near the hospital and
his work, without a family tying him down.

Maybe the physical picture of this made him stop and think.
Anyway, he said he wants to try to work on this marriage. He's
even agreed to seek professional help. I want our marriage to
work, and for the first time I think there's really a chance.

All this by way of saying I want to thank you more than
words can express for being there when I needed someone.

                    Sandra

Four years later they were still together. When I opened
Sandra's chart after watching the slides of her children, I
saw the letter. The back was painted in an abstract design
of yellows and pinks that looked as though she had taken a
sunset and swirled it all around. This was the woman I was
lying to.

Sandra thought she was seeing me for a routine checkup
after a pelvic infection. Actually, we took a culture from
her because a month earlier she had had a bad enough case
of gonorrhea to be admitted to the hospital. Now we had
to find out whether she was cured. Ted had given it to her.
It was his physician who called me, saying, "Dr. Stevens
wants to know if you can treat his wife without telling her
what she has."

I sat here thinking, "I don't want to destroy this marriage,
which I know is already on a shaky basis, yet I *am* with-
holding information that she's entitled to." Sandra knew
she'd had an infection; she'd had a high fever and abdominal
pain. But she still didn't know it was a venereal infection.

I have no idea what a lawyer would say if the story ever
got to him. She never really asked me, "Did I have a venereal

disease?" I suppose I'd have to tell her if she pinned me down. Maybe it's not my judgment to make, whether this marriage is worth saving, but that's the position I'm put in. Frankly, I think almost any marriage is worth saving. I just hope Sandra never asks.

11. Bonnie Levy

After a number of years in the business, an obstetrician develops a pretty good intuition about which woman is going to have a hard time with her pregnancy and delivery. But some of them really fool me.

If a patient is hyperreactive to pain and carries on whenever she gets a shot or has blood drawn, I often think, "I'm not looking forward to this pregnancy, we're going to have a terrible time of it, screaming and carrying on." The immature girl who brings her little pillow into the labor room, or her doll, is not prepared to have a baby and I sometimes wonder whose fault it is: her parents', her own, her husband's, *ours?* Worst of all is the dependent young lady who is accompanied by Mommy for nine months of pregnancy visits. Of course we never see her husband. It's Mother who sits out in the waiting room with her grown daughter, the two of them practically holding hands. To get that young lady into the examining room without her parent is a feat. I'm damn sure this girl is not going to do very well upstairs in labor. She'll yell, "I want my mommy, I want my mommy."

These overprotective mothers are filled with old wives' tales and misconceptions about pregnancy. Remember, things have changed a lot since the days when Mother was whisked into the hospital and Father had to stay downstairs. Mother can't imagine why her daughter wants that husband to be with her, and she certainly can't understand why *she's* not allowed upstairs. Back when Mother was laboring, she was probably snowed to the point where she didn't know anything that went on until twenty-four hours later when someone told her her baby had been born. And now her daughter wants to go to natural childbirth class, know everything and be awake. And the husband is going to watch?! She can't believe it.

After Mother's baby was born, she was in bed for thirteen days in the hospital. Bedpans were brought. Bed baths were given. And she was sent home on the fourteenth day, weak as a kitten, unable to walk. She had to have private nurses or help at home because she'd been in bed for thirteen days. Just get in bed for thirteen days *without* having a baby and see what happens to you. But now her daughter's going to get up the next morning. My God, her insides are going to fall out, according to Mother. Yet in five days, this young woman is home, feeling strong—except that Mother will try to put her in bed and recreate the conditions of twenty years ago.

When I make rounds at the hospital, this anxious mother is there for every visiting hour, and she always follows me outside with all the questions she has about her daughter: Is she really all right? Is the baby all right? Has the pediatrician seen the baby? Is that the best pediatrician in town? And she'll instruct me: "Now you tell my daughter that she has to have a nurse for at least the first three months after she comes home." *I'm* supposed to tell the daughter. I usually don't say very much. Sometimes I try to tell the mother to stop interfering, but that seldom works. It's easier just to say okay, fine, and then not mention anything to the daughter —or tell her to beware of a mother bearing gifts.

These mothers come in all the time, and I guess you could say they're the classic Jewish Mother. I'd say that more are Jewish than not, but they really don't have to be. Italian mothers, for example, are just as motherly. And one of my patients is a black lady from St. Croix whose kids call her "our Jewish mother."

I got Bonnie Levy as a patient when her mother became a gynecological patient of mine a few years ago. They sort of came as a package. From the first visit, Bonnie was normally accompanied by her mother.

Mrs. Garfinkel was a thin, dark-haired woman with plenty of money, a lot of expensive-looking jewelry and one daughter, Bonnie. A couple of years after I started seeing Mrs. Garfinkel, Bonnie got married and became Mrs. Sydney Levy. Mrs. Garfinkel thought Bonnie was too young to get married—she was twenty and had dropped out of Finch College —but at least Sydney came from a good family and his parents didn't try to run things. I don't know how Mr. Garfinkel felt because he was never mentioned.

Bonnie was quiet and seemed content enough, but I hadn't gotten to know her very well. I sometimes had the feeling she wasn't really quite there with me. She seldom showed any emotion and she had a funny little habit: if I asked her something—"How is everything, Bonnie?"—she'd answer politely with a word or two—"Fine, thank you"—and then she'd ask me in exchange: "How are you?" Like at a tea! Maybe it was just her way of maintaining her privacy. The only thing I knew she didn't like was the examining table.

Then, in October, a little more than a year after she was married, Bonnie and Mrs. Garfinkel came in and Bonnie said she thought she was pregnant. She had missed one period, and this was about two weeks later, so I examined her to make sure.

There are several things I do. Actually, I can just put my hand on her breast and almost tell right then; there's a certain feel to a pregnant breast. But when I feel that the uterus is slightly enlarged and soft on top, I know darn well the woman is pregnant.

If a lady thinks she's pregnant but my examination doesn't look positive, there are laboratory tests we can perform right in the office. There is a two-hour urine test called a UCG, which is definite proof. Before running that, however, we see whether we can get a clear reading from a simple but highly sensitive two-minute test called a Gravindex. A drop of urine, a drop of antiserum and two drops of a white chemical called antigen are mixed on a black slide. Mrs. Donohue then gently rotates the slide for two minutes, watching continuously. If the mixture stays milky and homogenous, it's a positive test. If tiny white particles form, it's negative. We really run that test more often for the patient's benefit than for ours. It's always nice for the patient to hear, "Your pregnancy test is positive." Then she's sure, because that's what she's been taught. Most times when we run a pregnancy test for ourselves, it's because we have a woman whose uterus is tipped back in midposition and we can't get hold of the top to feel if it's soft.

I was sure Bonnie was pregnant, but I didn't say anything until Katey came in and told me the Gravindex was positive. I told Katey to send Bonnie in. Mrs. Garfinkel came to my office door with Bonnie, and I was about to say something to her when Bonnie turned and said, "Mother, this is personal." So I thought, "Good for Bonnie, now we're getting somewhere." Mrs. Garfinkel returned to the waiting room.

Bonnie and I went into the office. When I told her she was pregnant, her face got all pink and shiny and she blushed furiously. She's a pretty girl, blonde, blue-eyed, with something of a baby-face. She has a tendency to be pudgy, which I guess she has to fight. She really doesn't look at all like Mrs. Garfinkel, although she dresses in the same conservative, expensive-looking manner. And for a young girl, she wears quite a lot of jewelry. She's always got a gold pin and earrings and one or two strands of pearls—and a great big pear-shaped diamond engagement ring that I guess shows what a good family Sydney comes from.

So there she sat, not saying much, just smiling and excited. And if she was up-tight during the exam—which is nothing unusual in a young girl who's suddenly throwing all caution to the wind with her legs spread wide apart and somebody looking at her—well, now she really seemed happy and kind of liberated. After all, she got pregnant by her husband, not her mother, so that gave her a little edge on Mother.

Anyway, I couldn't help feeling happy for her. At the same time, I was uneasy about the pregnancy, because Bonnie was immature to start with, and besides, I'm against people having babies so soon after they get married. If they ask me, I always tell couples, "You are going to be parents for the rest of your lives, but you're only husband and wife for a little while, so take a couple of years and *be* husband and wife. It makes a big difference in the family when that child arrives. Anybody who thinks otherwise doesn't have any children."

Finally Bonnie asked, "Dr. Sweeney, you're absolutely positive? I mean, it's definite?"

"It's definite, Bonnie."

"Oh, that's wonderful. I can't believe it. I can't wait to tell Syd. He won't believe it!"

"Why?" I asked.

She blushed. "Well, he *will*—I mean, this is the first time we tried, and it just happened."

I smiled. "Do you have any questions?"

She looked surprised and then shook her head, which is not unusual, because when I've just told a woman she's pregnant, she's so excited she can't remember her first name, let alone what her questions are. So I have a sort of spiel I usually deliver about pregnancy: I give the lady her vitamins and iron and tell her to keep her weight gain down to twenty pounds. She is not eating for two, that's an old wives' tale. And I explain what she *should* eat—the proteins and vegetables and things like that. I tell her she'll come back to be examined every four weeks until the seventh month, then every three weeks, then two weeks and then every week or more often if she needs it. I go through all this so when she's told at seven months to come back in three weeks, she won't suddenly exclaim: "Three weeks! What's wrong?" And I tell her not to expect to feel the baby move for four and a half to five and a half months. Otherwise she'll be convinced the baby's dead because it hasn't stirred when she's three months pregnant.

I try to anticipate what she's going to worry about. I always say there will be certain days when she won't feel so hot, and there may be some nausea. After all, something has to give as this uterus gets bigger, and the bowel and stomach get pushed out of the way. I say her back is going to ache and her feet sometimes will be swollen; and she'll have to go to the bathroom more often, including in the middle of the night. The discomfort will get worse as the uterus gets bigger and pushes on the bladder.

I explain that in the first part of pregnancy, nature wants her to slow down, so she becomes tired. In the middle third of pregnancy, everything's fine: suddenly the nausea is gone and she's got her energy back. But toward the end, it's going to happen all over again.

I try at this point not to mention the abnormal things. All the women have heard about them anyway. If I just say,

"Edema is a danger sign," they've all got swelling and excess fluid. So I don't bring it up as long as I'm watching each lady so closely. Obviously I tell her that if she has any bleeding she should let me know. And I always advise her to buy a book about pregnancy—but please not to concentrate on the section about abnormal obstetrics! I encourage her to go to some classes, whether or not she's thinking of natural childbirth, because she'll learn a lot. I also say that pregnancy is a physiological process; there's nothing pathological in being pregnant; you're not sick. But there are a lot of old wives' tales connected with pregnancies, and I tell her to call me if she has any problems. And finally I warn her: "Druggists are worthless; husbands don't know much; and mothers and mothers-in-law—forget it." The woman who comes into the hospital and has her gallbadder or appendix removed doesn't leave feeling she's an expert on these operations, but a lady has one baby and she'll be delighted to tell you all kinds of things about being pregnant, most of which are incorrect. Now, not every doctor runs a pregnancy the same way I do. I may be more liberal in some things and not as liberal in others. But once I've assumed responsibility for a lady's care, she's in my ball park and has to play by my rules.

Bonnie listened to all of this, nodding, and she didn't seem as filled with anxieties as I expected. "Bonnie," I said, "you're going to go home and talk to Sydney and I know darn well you're going to come up with a bunch of questions. Write them down and bring in your list next time so you don't forget them. And remember, you can call me if you want to ask something in the meantime."

"Thank you, Dr. Sweeney," Bonnie exclaimed. "Isn't it wonderful?"

I grinned. "Yeah, the whole thing's pretty wonderful."

I got up and hugged her and walked her to the door. And there was Mrs. Garfinkel waiting.

"I'm pregnant, Mommy," Bonnie said. "I'm really pregnant!"

"That's wonderful, sweetheart. I'm so happy for you—although I'm not sure I'm ready to be a grandmother yet. I'll have to get used to that idea."

Bonnie smiled. "You'll get used to it, Mommy. I'm not used to it either. Let's go somewhere so I can call Sydney."

Then Mrs. Garfinkel said to me, "Dr. Sweeney, I hope you told Bonnie she really ought to lose some weight."

"I don't think this is quite the time for Bonnie to try to *lose* weight, Mrs. Garfinkel. But we talked about keeping her weight gain down during her pregnancy."

We were still standing in the doorway to my office and Mrs. Garfinkel asked, "Did you tell her no medicine—she's not to take any pills from now on?"

"Yes, I told her she shouldn't take anything she doesn't have to. Bonnie," I added, "that doesn't mean you have to sit around with a splitting headache because you're afraid to take an aspirin. If you have any questions, call me."

Mrs. Garfinkel still had a hand on my arm, but Bonnie said, "Mommy, I'm going to call Sydney. Are you coming or not?"

Two weeks later, I got a phone call from Mrs. Garfinkel: "Dr. Sweeney, you've got to tell Bonnie to stop drinking."

"What's she drinking?"

"Alcohol," said Mrs. Garfinkel, sounding as if it were cyanide. "Bonnie and Sydney were over for dinner last night and she wanted a cocktail. I told her it wasn't good for her, but she said you told her it was all right."

"That's true, Mrs. Garfinkel. I told Bonnie if she felt like having a drink before dinner, she could. And if it made her feel sick, not to have one. She also asked me about smoking, and I told her it would be better if she could stop but I didn't think the six or eight cigarettes a day she smokes would hurt the baby. I told her I wouldn't suggest that she take any *trips. . . ."*

Now that was kind of mean, to put the idea into Mrs. Garfinkel's head that her little girl might be taking trips. But she said, "Trips! I didn't know she and Sydney were planning any trips!" So she didn't understand the slang to begin with. When I'd mentioned marijuana to Bonnie, she told me she had tried it once but nothing had happened and she'd never smoked it again. Which is good because we just don't know what effect marijuana or any of the other drugs these kids might be using will have on their progeny.

Mrs. Garfinkel accompanied Bonnie on all of her following checkup visits, and something strange seemed to be happening. After that first visit when she learned she was pregnant, Bonnie seemed to be putting herself more and more into her mother's hands.

In November, Mrs. Garfinkel told me Bonnie's apartment was scheduled to be painted. "I certainly don't think Bonnie should be inhaling all those paint fumes, do you, Dr. Sweeney?"

I turned to Bonnie and said, "The paint can't hurt you, but if the smell makes you feel sick, maybe you want to put it off."

But Mrs. Garfinkel arranged then and there for Bonnie and Sydney to stay in her guest room while her maid oversaw the painting and cleaned up afterward.

After the Christmas and New Year's holidays, Mrs. Garfinkel brought up the question of Bonnie's weight again: "She ate everything and gained three pounds."

"Maybe you want to sit in here behind my desk and let me stand out there, Mrs. Garfinkel," I said, "because you're doing a better job than I am. You're harder on Bonnie."

But Bonnie simply nodded, and that's how it went. I began to think it was just stubborn of me to insist on talking to

Bonnie alone. The three of us always ended up in the hallway
going over Mrs. Garfinkel's questions.

I suggested to Bonnie at one point that she might want to
bring Sydney with her. I prefer to see the husband at least
once so I can tell him everything's going all right and answer
his questions. After all, his wife goes home and says, "Dr.
Sweeney says I'm fine," but the husband is not really sure. I
get extra phone calls at the office between six and seven at
night, because a husband comes home from work and says,
"Did you ask the doctor if we can take that drive this weekend?"

"No, I forgot."

"Well, call him. That's what you're paying him for."

So I like to meet him at least once. It's bad enough for the
husband to show up at a hospital he's not familiar with when
his wife's in labor. Then if he doesn't even know what his
doctor looks like, it's kind of ridiculous.

Bonnie said, "Syd's awfully busy, Dr. Sweeney. But I'll
see."

I don't know whether she asked him or not, but he didn't
show up. Just Mrs. Garfinkel came, and on one visit it was,
"What about her veins, Dr. Sweeney? Are her legs going to
get worse?"

I could have belted her. I knew she wasn't being intention-
ally mean. Mrs. Garfinkel obviously loved her daughter, but
she certainly wasn't helping Bonnie. And I couldn't say anything except that it was hard to tell about the veins. They
do get worse in pregnancy because the big pregnant uterus
is in the way and the blood can't get back from the legs.

The morning Bonnie was in for her second two-week visit
—she was due the third week of June—Laura, my nurse,
murmured as I went into the examining room, "Here's Bonnie Levy's chart. Mrs. Garfinkel is missing in action." I guess
I showed my surprise because she added, "Don't look at me.
I didn't do anything with her. Bonnie came alone."

I examined Bonnie and then we went back into my office to talk. I told her everything was fine and asked how she felt.

"I feel huge, Dr. Sweeney. And I waddle. I can't even walk right. Mom says I don't have to waddle like that. But I can't seem to help it."

At that, I just blew up. "Bonnie, your mother probably means well, but she's making things hard on you and she's driving *me* crazy. What's she talking about now? You're eight months pregnant and you've got this big thing out in front. Of course you waddle because you've got to walk with your back arched or you'll fall flat on your face. All pregnant women walk like that. It's called a lordotic position. It's to balance against the weight in front of your center of gravity. If your mother says she carried you around without waddling, either she's got a damn poor memory or she's lying to herself and to you. Where is she, anyway?"

Bonnie burst into tears, and I thought, "Oh my God, what have I done?" But then she started laughing at the same time and she managed to say, "I didn't tell her I had an appointment and she's going to be furious that I waddled in here all alone."

She was really laughing now, and she got the hiccups besides, so we took a few minutes to get a glass of water and let her settle down. Then we finally talked.

"Dr. Sweeney, it's not just my mother. Sydney and I haven't been together for a few months, and I just feel so lonely."

"Where's Sydney?"

"He's nowhere. I mean, he's home, but we just haven't been together."

"What does that mean?"

"I mean—we stopped going to bed together several months ago."

Well, that could be real trouble. There's a certain aura

about pregnancy: even in the hospital if a doctor in some other department gets a pregnant woman on his floor, he's panicked. Some husbands are also afraid of pregnant ladies. They lose their sex drive by the time their wives are pregnant for five or six months. And many cheat. If you tell them they *can* have intercourse, they shut it off. If you tell them they can't, they go somewhere else to get it. But I didn't know what was going on with Bonnie and Sydney, so I just asked, "Did Sydney tell you why he wasn't going to bed with you?"

She looked surprised. "He didn't have to," she said. "*I* told *him* we shouldn't. My mother said I could have a miscarriage. She said it happened to her. I never knew she had a miscarriage before."

"Oh my God, Bonnie, that's a lot of garbage. You're a big girl and you've got to learn to take your mother with a grain of salt. Now will you please listen to me. Different doctors may say different things, but as far as I'm concerned, you can make love the night before you go into labor. Just cut it out in the labor room because you might embarrass somebody. Don't tell Sydney—let's just keep this between you and me—but no man in the world is big enough to reach the cervix or rupture the membranes. So it's fine for the two of you to be together as long as it's fun and comfortable. He can't hurt you, and he can't hurt your baby."

She looked pretty happy about that. She blushed and admitted, "We've done other things, but I want to make *love* with him."

"Well, go home and make love." I grinned. "Take the phone off the hook. You're lucky you're not a doctor so you can do it. What else do you want to talk about?"

"I think I should tell you I'm scared."

It wasn't bad to have that come out. All pregnant women are afraid and I told her so.

"But I'm scared of so many things," she said. "If I tell you about all the things, you'll think I'm crazy."

"No I won't. I'll think you're about to be a mother. Now what are you scared of?"

"The main thing I want is for the baby to be all right," she said. "But I want to be good about everything too, and I don't know how I'm going to act. I don't think I'm very good about pain."

"We'll give you an anesthetic in the last part of your labor so the pain will hardly bother you."

"But—I know I'm being impossible. Sydney says I'm being impossible. Everyone says I'm being impossible—"

"You're not being impossible."

"Well, I want to see our baby born." She stopped as if she had presented an insurmountable problem.

I told her there are several kinds of anesthetic that take away the pain and still leave the lady wide-awake. We would give her one of those. "What else is on your mind?" I asked.

"I was wondering when I should call you."

"You mean when you go into labor?"

"Yes. Assuming I can tell. I guess I'll know," she added hesitantly.

"You'll know. You'll have abdominal pains. Then when you put your hands on your stomach, it'll be getting hard. You can call me as soon as labor starts. Or after the pains get pretty regular, you can time them and call me when they're coming about every ten minutes. Remember, I said *about* ten minutes. It doesn't have to be ten minutes exactly."

I remember one patient who taught me to be clear on this point. When she finally got in touch with me, the pains were coming every four minutes. "But I told you to call when they were coming every ten," I said.

"They came at twelve and eight and six, and now they're four," she answered. "They never *came* at ten."

"Now Bonnie, you understand that once the water breaks, whether or not you've felt any contractions, you call me right away. And get in bed if you don't reach me immediately."

"When does the water usually break?"

"It can happen any time."

"My God," said Bonnie, "what if I'm in the middle of Bloomingdale's?"

"You'll get wet and come over here in a taxi."

She smiled and then became serious again.

"Okay, let's have it," I said.

"Dr. Sweeney," she asked solemnly, "what will happen if you're not there when the baby's coming?"

"I'll be there, Bonnie. My service can always get in touch with me."

She smiled and thanked me for "spending so much time with a nut like me" and said she was going to ask Sydney to come with her next time.

"That'll be swell," I answered and kissed her on the cheek when we said good-bye. "Have a nice night," I added, and she blushed deep pink.

It's not unusual for women to fear their doctor will miss the delivery. Of course no patient should expect the doctor to be in constant attendance from the onset of labor. He may be in the operating room, or with other patients, or sleeping. And the nurse who has seen a lot of women in labor doesn't want to wake a doctor at two o'clock in the morning for a patient who's not going to deliver until three the next afternoon. But occasionally they make mistakes. I've had a resident or nurse phone me and say, "Your patient, Mrs. So-and-so, just came in and she looks like she's got about four hours to go." So I roll over and go back to sleep, or continue seeing patients, and suddenly I'll get a frantic call: "Your patient's ready for delivery."

I'll say, "I'm on my way, but if I'm late, *don't you hold the baby back.*"

This is actually done in some places. The lady's about to deliver and the doctor's not there, so that baby is literally held back—or the nurses will cross the lady's legs. The baby is in there trying to be born. It may take two or three breaths in the vagina, where there isn't any oxygen, and may suffer brain damage. It's inexcusable to delay a delivery. There's always somebody at the hospital who can take over.

We don't miss many deliveries, but anybody who's in obstetrics misses an occasional one. I've never faked it, but there are some doctors who do. When the patient is ready for delivery and her doctor isn't there, she's given some anesthesia that puts her out and she is delivered by a different obstetrician. Then her own doctor comes roaring in with his white coat on, takes some blood—there's always plenty of blood around, with the placenta and episiotomy—and he smears it over him and acts as if he's just finished the delivery. He walks out to greet the father and says, "It's a boy." I've seen it done.

I don't think too much of such a doctor, but what am I going to do? I can't go out and say to the parents, "Ha ha, he wasn't there. . . ." Doctors are people, and there are thieves among all of us, I guess. We all want to be present for the delivery. This is my patient. She came to me and she's paying for my care, so missing the delivery makes me a little mad. Some mothers are understanding but others are angry, and I don't blame them. I just think that I might as well own up to it: "I wasn't there." In a year, which probably means about 170 deliveries, it happens only once or twice.

Late in the afternoon, Mrs. Garfinkel phoned me: "Dr. Sweeney, I heard Bonnie was in to see you today. I don't understand why she came without me, but I want to know how she is."

"Mrs. Garfinkel," I replied, "you've got a grown-up daughter. I don't have any secrets from Bonnie. If you want to know what the story is, call Bonnie and ask her."

I had had it with Mrs. Garfinkel.

12. Three-Ring Circus

By June 30, Bonnie Levy was two and a half weeks late delivering. A lot of women get nervous or even angry when that happens. It's pretty unfair in a way: a woman has made her bargain with nature for forty weeks of lugging this big bulk around and she's really ready to get rid of it. Everyone is asking her, "When are you due?" And she says, "Anytime now," or "Yesterday!" And nothing happens. When her family and friends don't hear anything for a few days, they call again, thinking they missed the big news. And there's this lady, still at home, still big and fat and waddling to the phone to hear someone say, "My goodness, I didn't think you'd be home *already,* what did you have?"

"I don't know, I still haven't had it," she says. By this time she figures her baby is going to be born ready for kindergarten. Finally her husband, or in Bonnie's case, her mother, says, "My God, when are you going to deliver? Don't you think you should be induced?"

Two and a half weeks is late enough to consider induction, but the delay didn't seem to be upsetting Bonnie. When we talked every couple of days, she would tell me all the things she was doing since she had this extra time. During the last weeks of pregnancy, many women find the very thought of food slightly revolting. But Bonnie, who had never been much of a cook, was trying new recipes and freezing dinners so there would be food in the house when she came home from the hospital. "The only trouble is, my stomach gets in the way, and everything I cook has to be on the front burners," she said.

I told her if she was in the middle of cooking when she went into labor, I trusted she'd stop and come to the hospital. I've had women in labor finish a roast or clean the house or order the week's groceries before they would come in. I've sat there waiting while my patient was going over a marketing list. I've even had ladies call me in labor to say they'd leave for the hospital right after they did their hair!

Bonnie finally phoned midafternoon on the last day of June to say she'd had a bloody discharge, or show. This is a mucousy substance tinged with blood which is dislodged from the cervix as it begins to dilate. Typically, this discharge heralds the onset of labor, although several hours may pass before real labor begins. Bonnie said she didn't have any cramps.

"What are you doing?" I asked.

"I'm making chocolate chip cookies."

"In this heat!"

"Well, Sydney likes them, and if I have to go to the hospital, I want him to have some homemade cookies to eat."

I told her to lie down and in a couple of hours to let me know what was happening.

"Okay, this is the last batch anyway," she said.

At five o'clock she called again. I was over at the hospital with another obstetrical patient, Polly Andrews, so they put the call through there. Bonnie said she felt like she had a mild stomachache and she had to go to the bathroom every few minutes.

"Has your water broken?" I asked. "Do you think that's what it is?"

"I don't know. I just keep going to the bathroom."

"What color is it? If it's yellow, it's urine. But if it's colorless, then your membranes have ruptured, and you ought to come in."

"I can't tell what color it is," she said. "We have those Daisy things in the toilets and they make the water blue so I can't see anything!"

I laughed. "Get a clear bowl and use that next time. Then call me back." I gave Bonnie the hospital number and told her to ask for the delivery floor.

At 5:30 P.M., she called again. "I've got some of it right here in a bowl, Dr. Sweeney. I'm looking at it and it doesn't look like urine to me."

"Okay—"

And I heard Sydney in the background saying, "It doesn't look like urine to me, either."

"Okay, I guess Sydney's home. Well, don't spend any more time looking at the bowl, the two of you, come on in."

Once the amniotic sac has broken, the baby loses his protective cushion of about half a gallon of amniotic fluid. More important, when the membranes rupture, the umbilical cord can prolapse, or fall out. In any case, the baby is no longer sealed off as effectively from the outside world. I wanted Bonnie in the hospital, where she would best be guarded against uterine infection, and where I could watch her and induce her if she didn't soon go into spontaneous labor.

The Levys arrived an hour later, at 6:30 P.M. I was with Polly Andrews when one of the nurses told me Mrs. Levy had checked in. I couldn't leave Polly at that point, so I just said, "Have the resident look at Bonnie and tell her I'll be there in a little while." Then I kind of mumbled, "What'd they do anyway, walk here?"

I didn't expect an answer, but the nurse had one: "No, Mrs. Levy said Sydney hadn't had dinner so she gave him something to eat first because she felt fine. She didn't eat anything herself, though, and she says now she's hungry."

"No food," I said. "And tell whoever examines her to talk to me."

A few minutes later the nurse came back to say Mrs. Garfinkel was on the phone. "Do I look like I can talk to Mrs. Garfinkel?" I snapped. I had my hand in Polly's vagina at that point. "Tell her I don't talk to mothers, anyway, unless I'm delivering them."

The nurse went out in a hurry and I knew she'd say something more respectable to Mrs. Garfinkel.

At a quarter to seven, the resident came in to say he had examined Bonnie. She was 2 centimeters and indeed her membranes had ruptured. I went down the hall to look in on her, leaving the resident with Polly.

Bonnie was sitting up reading when I walked in. "Dr. Sweeney, how are *you*?"

"I'm fine, Bonnie. How are you feeling?"

"I think I'm hungry. At least I was hungry until a few minutes ago. Now I'm not sure."

"Where's Sydney?"

"He went to see if I could change to rooming-in. I'd really like to keep the baby with me in the hospital, but they have to see if there's a bed available."

"That's quite a lot of work, rooming-in."

She looked daggers at me. "You sound like Mother!"

"Is that a nice thing to say to your obstetrician?"

She laughed. "I had one real pain," she said. "It was kind of scary. I felt like somebody was scraping their nails inside my stomach. But the rest of the time, there's been practically nothing."

"Okay, Bonnie. It's still very early, you know. You're just beginning labor. The nurse or one of the doctors will be coming in all the time, and I'll see you later this evening. I've got another lady right down the hall who's going to have her baby ahead of you."

Bonnie popped upright in bed. "Boy, would I love to see that!"

"I bet you would. But you're staying put. Read your magazine and I'll see you later."

I went back to Polly Andrews, two rooms away. I had been watching Polly with special concern as she approached the end of her pregnancy. Her pelvis was narrow and the question was whether the head of the good-sized baby she was carrying would be able to fit through, or whether we would have to do a Caesarean section. When I had examined Polly a week ago, the baby's head was just dipping, not yet engaged between the pelvic bones. I ordered a pelvic series: X-rays of the pelvis in various planes. While we obviously don't want to X-ray anybody unnecessarily, in this case I had no choice. I had to know the size of the head in relationship to the size and shape of the pelvis.

The specialist who read the complicated series sent the X-rays to my office with the comment, "It's a borderline pelvis. With good labor, the head might come through. But it's sure going to be close."

Polly went into labor early this morning and immediately came to the hospital. She understood the situation: we would have to wait and watch the baby's progress, then make our decision about how to deliver it. One thing made me feel bad: Polly's husband didn't stay with her. When he brought her to the hospital in the morning, he asked me if there was some special reason he should stay. I figured if he didn't know, it wasn't up to me to tell him. I said anyway, "It will probably be a long wait for her, and she might be glad to have the company."

This guy—his name is Michael, but I was calling him Mr. Andrews—actually went to Polly and asked, "Do you think I'd better stick around, hon?"

Now she was scared to death to begin with. But I guess she was used to his ways. She just said, "No, Mike, you go ahead to the office. We can always call you when something starts to happen."

I saw patients in my office until quarter past two in the afternoon, when the hospital phoned. Polly had started good labor. I walked the seven blocks to the Lying-In unit, examined Polly and said I'd see her again in a little while.

At 4 P.M. I was back at the hospital. Polly's cervix was 3 centimeters dilated. She had an infusion in her arm. Her blood had already been cross-matched and a supply for possible transfusion was on call. It was still too early to know whether she would be able to deliver vaginally.

I suggested to Polly that I phone Mike. There are no telephones in the labor rooms. She agreed eagerly. I guess she had been wanting to ask him to come for some time. Mike Andrews arrived around 5:15 P.M. By 5:45, Polly's cervix was over 5 centimeters dilated. Her contractions were strong. The baby's head was now engaged into the pelvis but not descending through the dilating cervix. I ruptured her membranes with a membrane hook, which is like a long, thin crocheting needle. It fits up, curved end first, into the cervix. As I brought it down, the hook ruptured the sac. Some of the amniotic fluid came out.

Polly continued in good labor, but when I examined her

at 6:15 P.M., the baby's head was still not descending, although her cervix was 6 centimeters dilated.

Now, at ten to seven, I stood outside Polly's room and studied the X-rays on the view box on the wall. Mike Andrews was next to me.

"I want to examine Polly once more," I said. "If the head still isn't descending, I won't wait any longer. We've given it a fair trial."

Mrs. Ames, the labor nurse, and I checked Polly again. Outside in the corridor, I told Mrs. Ames in front of Mike, "The baby's not coming down through that pelvis. I'll section her as soon as you're ready."

Mrs. Ames notified the resident, who would make all the calls to get an operating room team to assist me. It wouldn't take long. Day or night we can begin operating within ten minutes from the moment an emergency call goes in.

As soon as Mike and I walked into Polly's room, she looked at us and knew. Her eyes filled with tears. "I have to have a Caesarean," she said.

I nodded. "There's nothing wrong with having a baby abdominally instead of vaginally, Polly. You and the baby are both in good shape. We tried, but the baby is just not going to make it through your pelvis."

"Will I always have to have a Caesarean?" she asked.

"That's hard to say. Your pelvis isn't going to get any bigger, but if your next baby is smaller, you will probably be able to delivery vaginally. Even if you can't, there's no limit to the number of Caesarean sections a woman can have."

I left Polly and Mike alone for a couple of minutes.

Polly signed permission for the Caesarean section. Mrs. Ames gave her an injection of atropine to dry her throat and windpipe secretions. Two nurse's aides wheeled an operating table into Polly's labor room, transferred her to it and wheeled her back around the corner to the OR rooms. Mike said good-bye to Polly and I told him to wait downstairs in her room on the private obstetrical floor.

When I walked into the operating room, scrubbed and ready for my sterile gown and gloves, Polly was lying on the table. Her abdomen, rising in a white mound, had been shaved and washed with disinfectants. Her arms were spread-eagled on supports at right angles from her body so that we could have immediate access to her veins if necessary. In an emergency, we wouldn't want her arms by her sides, buried under layers of sterile drapes. An infusion was running into Polly's left hand, but she was awake because we didn't want to sedate the baby. Once we put Polly to sleep, we wouldn't have much time to get the baby out.

Two doctors were assisting me at the table: Dr. Susan Perry, a fourth-year GYN resident, and an intern I hadn't worked with before. Dr. Marcham, a good man, was the anesthesiologist. Also present were the operating room nurses and a delivery force—a doctor and two nurses—to take the baby from me.

"How long will this take?" Polly asked.

I was at the table on her left.

"Do you mean until we get the baby out or until you wake up?" I responded.

"Until you get my baby out," Polly said.

"Two minutes from the time you go to sleep."

"Two minutes," Polly exclaimed. "That sounds impossible."

"If an obstetrician can't get a baby out in two minutes, he ought to go shuffle papers."

The intern made a muffled sound behind his mask. I glanced at him and he dropped his eyes quickly. Polly was smiling. "How long until I wake up?"

"A little over an hour," I said.

The scrub nurse helped me cover Polly with a sterile green

sheet. A narrow rectangular window was precut into it. We positioned this opening over her abdomen where I would make the incision. The top of the sheet rested over a square frame above Polly's head, keeping the drape off her face and blocking her view.

"Will you let Mike know if everything's okay?" Polly asked.

"Of course," I said.

Dr. Marcham injected Pentothal directly into the infusion tubing.

"How are you, Polly?" he asked.

"I'm still awake." A few seconds later she said, "I'm still here."

Then she stopped talking. Dr. Marcham ran his finger across her eyelashes and asked, "Are you asleep?"

There was no response. He put the black oxygen mask over her nose and mouth. I glanced at the clock. It was fifteen seconds past 7:25 P.M. Dr. Marcham ran his finger over her lashes again and said, "Okay."

The nurse handed me a scalpel and I made an incision from the symphysis, which is the bone at the bottom of the pelvis. The cut went almost to the navel. The used knife banged into a pan as the nurse handed me a new one. I went down quickly through the abdominal layers, clamping off a few blood vessels, until I got to the uterus. I put a Balfour retractor, which looks like a shoehorn bent at a right angle, into the bottom of the incision to spread it. Then I cut across the front of the uterus and pushed the bladder out of the way. Next I made a small incision into the uterus, down to the amniotic fluid. Dr. Perry suctioned out the liquid and blood accumulating in front of the retractor. I put two fingers into the small uterine incision, stretching or pulling instead of cutting it apart. That way I wouldn't cut into any large blood vessels.

Putting my left hand into the uterus, I felt the hot moistness there and then the rounded form of the baby's head. It was face down. I felt for the chin and turned the head to help keep the baby from sucking any fluid. Besides, if I brought it out face up, we could suction its mouth and nose faster. Dr. Perry was pushing down on top of the uterus to give me some leverage. I slid my hand behind the baby's head, feeling the back of its neck, and I lifted. The head came out slowly, topped by a shock of brown hair. We had it made! If it took a while to get the rest of the baby out, okay: the baby could breathe.

Dr. Perry immediately inserted the brownish-red bulb syringe into the baby's mouth, suctioning mucus. I slid my right hand along its back, supporting the shoulders as I brought them out sideways. The rest of the baby's body slid out and I had her in a half-sitting position, my left hand behind the head and neck, my right hand cupped under her buttocks. Streaks of blood showed bright red against the white, sticky coating of vernix that covered her skin.

Dr. Perry had barely inserted the bulb syringe into the baby's nostril when her first short squawking cry broke the silence of the room. More short, sharp squawks.

"Two minutes. Son-of-a-bitch," the intern said glancing at the clock. His spontaneous comment ended in a gulp when he realized he'd spoken out loud.

"Clamps," I said.

Dr. Perry clamped and cut the thick bluish umbilical cord, leaving a long piece hanging from the baby. The delivery room doctor took the little girl immediately from my hands and into an adjoining room. The baby deserved a sterile room of her own, where the cord would be reclamped close to the umbilicus and she would be examined, weighed, cleaned, banded and footprinted.

"She looks like a good girl," I said to Dr. Perry, grinning under my mask.

She nodded, eyes smiling back briefly. The intern reached for the suction tube.

"Get the Pit on," I said.

Dr. Marcham switched a carefully controlled amount of Pitocin into the infusion to help the uterus contract. It did, muscles clamping tight across the blood vessels going from the uterine wall into the placenta. Not only was the blood supply cut off by the contractions, but the area within the uterus where the placenta was attached was being diminished. The placenta, unable to shrink correspondingly, separated and was pushed out. It was a mass of grayish-white, wound with thick blue veins. It went into a tray for the Path Lab.

I brought the uterus up through the incision, lightly massaging it round and round with the flat of my hands, then with my thumbs. It looked like a large, round dark-pink softball. Difficult to believe a seven- or eight-pound infant had just come out of there.

At 7:29, we started the long procedure of cleaning and repairing the uterus and abdominal cavity. Two minutes could get the baby out, but over an hour of work remained before Polly would be ready for the recovery room. When the delivery room doctor came in to tell me the baby was fine, I told him to call Mike Andrews. It didn't seem fair to keep Mike waiting until I would be through and could talk to him myself.

At 8 P.M., Mrs. Ames came into the operating room. Mrs. Lincoln, a patient of mine who was due in a week, had telephoned. She thought she might be in labor.

"Tell her to come to the hospital," I said. Judy Lincoln had had her first two babies by natural childbirth—two of the easiest pregnancies and deliveries I'd seen. If she thought she might be in labor, I'd better examine her.

We were still putting in sutures, almost ready to close Polly's abdominal skin, when Mrs. Ames came in again. The

Lincolns had arrived. The resident had examined Judy and she was ready to deliver.

"Ready to deliver!" I repeated in disbelief. "She didn't know if she was in labor."

I asked Dr. Perry to finish closing. Then I stripped off my gown and gloves, thanked everyone in the room, and followed Mrs. Ames outside.

"How's Bonnie Levy?" I asked as we trotted around the corner toward the labor rooms.

"She's fine," Mrs. Ames said. She shot me a glance. "Her mother came up onto the delivery floor while you were operating. We had to throw her out."

"Sorry I missed that," I said, silently blessing steady, professional Mrs. Ames, who handled everything from emergencies to unwelcome mothers.

At half-past eight, I was examining Judy Lincoln in the delivery room. She's a tall strawberry blonde, a lovely lady. She was 8 centimeters dilated. "I thought I was getting the twenty-four-hour virus," she said. "I didn't even want to bring my overnight bag with me."

Forty minutes later, after three contractions and one shot of Novocaine, Judy delivered a seven-and-a-half-pound girl. Her husband was there for the main event. They both held the baby and named her Jennifer on the spot. We let them all rest in the delivery room for a while.

Mrs. Ames commented quietly, "If we'd known your schedule for the evening, we'd have put on a double shift, doctor."

"You're doing just fine, Mrs. Ames," I told her.

I was walking down the corridor to Bonnie Levy's room when I heard a scream. Just one loud, sharp scream. Sydney came running out and I practically collided with him. I yelled, "Nurse," and went into the room.

"Please. I need something. It hurts," Bonnie gasped. She was ashen from the contraction she had just had.

"Get me a hundred milligrams of Demerol," I told the nurse. I handed her Bonnie's chart. "Wait a minute, where's the infusion?"

"There was none ordered, doctor."

"Well, I want one. I always want one."

The nurse went out.

Bonnie had recovered from the contraction. "Did that other lady have her baby?" she asked.

"Both ladies had their babies," I corrected her.

"Both!" she said.

I nodded, grinning. "Two mothers, two lovely little girls."

"Oh, I wish I would hurry up," Bonnie said. "I don't care what we have as long as it's all right," she added.

"I'm sure of that, Bonnie. Now try to get a little rest."

The nurse returned with the Demerol and I went to the desk to check on Polly Andrews. They had just taken her out of recovery to her own room. I walked two flights downstairs to look in on her and Mike.

Polly was dozing. Mike stepped out of the room to talk to me.

"Congratulations," I said.

"Thanks, Dr. Sweeney. Polly was awfully scared about this baby." He hesitated. "I'm glad our baby's healthy. She's not —she's not very *pretty*, I guess, but I'm glad it all went well."

Then I got angry. I grabbed Mike Andrews by the arm —he's about a foot taller than I am, lean and well groomed, like an attractive politician—and I said, "Come on, there's something you ought to see."

I hustled him down the stairs to the Pediatrics division, along the corridor, past the patients' rooms. We slammed through the swinging doors of the nursery and I stopped outside a small room marked Intensive Care. There were three babies, each in an enclosed incubator where the oxygen level was being regulated. I pointed to the closest incubator in which a tiny purplish infant lay motionless, two tubes running into her neck.

"That little girl was born last week with a heart defect. She's purple because her blood doesn't have enough oxygen. The condition is inoperable and it'll get progressively worse until she dies. That," I said, "is what you might call an ugly baby if you happen to think birth abnormalities and death are ugly."

Mike Andrews backed away from the window and started to cry. I waited it out.

"I get the point, Dr. Sweeney," he finally said.

Leaving Mike at Polly's room, I returned to the eighth floor and telephoned my wife.

"I remember you," she kidded. "Let me see if the Feinbergs do."

"Oh my God, the Feinbergs!" I suddenly realized they had been invited for dinner. My watch was in my clothes locker, and I craned my head around to see the wall clock. It was 10:15 P.M. "Tell them I'm sorry," I said.

"Where are you? At the hospital?"

"This is no hospital. It's a three-ring circus. I don't know when I'll be home."

"Why should tonight be different?" Fran asked. "You missed steak again."

Suddenly I was starving. I said good-bye and ducked into the Solarium, where I had to settle for two cups of coffee and a couple of sandwiches. I stayed in the Solarium and dictated my operative notes into the tape recorder there.

A little after 11 P.M., I went back to Bonnie. She had had another shot of Demerol but was uncomfortable and apprehensive. "It doesn't stop the pain, Dr. Sweeney," she said. Her mouth sounded dry from the medication. "I'm sorry to complain, but the pain is still there. It just comes through a haze. I feel as though I don't know what's happening."

I called Mrs. Ames and examined Bonnie. She was 6 centimeters dilated, having contractions every four minutes. I didn't want to give her any more Demerol.

"I don't suppose Dr. Marcham is still around," I asked Mrs. Ames.

"He certainly is," she said. "He's just finishing up with Dr. Abrams on an emergency ectopic. Dr. Abrams was set to do her tomorrow morning but she ruptured. We were going to call you if Dr. Abrams couldn't get here in time."

An ectopic or tubal pregnancy is one in which the fertilized egg starts to grow in the fallopian tube. The tube can't expand and may rupture before you can remove it, producing internal bleeding and sending the patient into shock.

I weighed Bonnie's situation. She probably had about four more hours of labor. Her main problem was fear of pain. I asked Mrs. Ames to have Dr. Marcham set up for an epidural when he finished in the OR room. Then I went back to Bonnie.

"We're going to give you what's called an epidural in a little while," I told her. "After that, you'll really be comfortable. It's a very good anesthetic. But you'll have to lie absolutely still and do exactly what Dr. Marcham tells you to."

"I won't move a muscle," Bonnie promised. "But I hope he's planning to do it between contractions."

Dr. Marcham arrived.

"She's six centimeters," I said. "She's coming along pretty fast for a primip, so I think we can do this now." Because the epidural stops the pain of the contractions and reduces the muscle power, it tends to slow down labor a little.

Bonnie looked at me. "Do you really think I'm coming along 'fast'?"

"I had a woman a couple of weeks ago who was in labor for nineteen hours."

Bonnie's eyes widened. Then she asked, "This won't put me to sleep, will it?"

Dr. Marcham reassured her, and we asked Sydney to wait outside. Mrs. Ames turned Bonnie over on her side in a fetal position, and Dr. Marcham prepped her back with disinfectant. Right over the backbone at waist level, he gave her an injection to numb the skin. Then he carefully inserted the Tuohy needle, a curved, blunt-ended needle, deep enough to reach but not penetrate the tough ligament that runs the length of the back. Attaching a syringe to the needle, he gently pushed into the epidural space surrounding the spinal fluid and injected 1 cc of local anesthetic. He turned the needle so the curved end pointed down, then threaded a narrow, flexible tube through it and injected 15 cc's of local anesthetic. This amount would last about an hour. Withdrawing the needle but leaving the catheter in place, Dr. Marcham would be able to renew the anesthetic when Bonnie needed it.

The epidural works quickly. Dr. Marcham waited with his hand on Bonnie's stomach until she had a contraction. *"Now,"* he said, "can you feel anything now?"

She hesitated. "I can feel some pressure way down, but it doesn't hurt." She looked at us, smiling and relieved. "I was so frightened the pain would keep getting worse."

I thanked Dr. Marcham and he left.

"Sydney got me onto the rooming-in floor." Bonnie sounded pleased.

"That's quite a gung-ho group," I said. It's a four-bed module, with each infant in a bassinet alongside the mother's bed. The mothers bathe, feed and change their babies, under a nurse's supervision, of course.

"Don't you think I can be gung-ho?" Bonnie asked.

"I'm sure you can." I was glad she was feeling better.

"Do the babies stay in the room overnight?"

"No, they're put in a separate nursery," Sydney said.

"What if you're breast-feeding?"

I looked at Bonnie in surprise. The last I'd heard, she'd planned to bottle-feed.

"They bring the babies in to the mothers," I explained. "You can't do it long distance, you know."

"Well, I'm going to be breast-feeding," Bonnie announced.

"When did you change your mind?" I asked.

"When Sydney went to change my room." Bonnie looked at me searchingly. "Don't you think I can do it?"

"Sure you can do it. That's what they were made for."

"How long do you usually breast-feed?" she asked.

"As long as everything's convenient and going well. But sooner or later these kids grow teeth, and nursing hurts after that."

Bonnie smiled.

"I'm serious," I said. "It's enough to have your breast gummed, but to have it chawed on is pretty uncomfortable. You don't have to nurse these kids until their bar mitzvah. Most people, after three or four months, want to quit."

"Oh, I'm sure that will be long enough," Bonnie said.

"There's nothing wrong with nursing part-time and using the bottle other times," I commented. "That way you can go out and not have to run right home to feed the baby. Of course it's your decision. But then you can let Daddy get up at two o'clock in the morning and take the bottle feeding. It's his kid too. The only problem is you're going to wake up because your breasts will be full of milk."

Sydney said, "You've got a nice helpful touch while you're letting people make their own decision, Dr. Sweeney."

I laughed. "Okay, I just wanted you to get the picture."

"I'm wide-awake," Bonnie announced.

"I can see that. But maybe if I go out, you'll rest a little."

I left, telling Mrs. Ames I was going to grab a nap and to

wake me in a couple of hours—or sooner if necessary. There are cots in the staff quarters over the operating floor, and since I was getting a cold and scheduled to operate in the morning besides, I thought the sleep would do me good. It didn't look as though I would get home tonight.

At 2 A.M., there was a knock on the door and I jolted awake.

"Mrs. Ames said you wanted a call," a young nurse said. The shift had changed at midnight.

Bonnie was tired when I went to see her. She lay quietly, saying very little. I examined her and said I thought we'd be taking her to the delivery room in about an hour.

"An hour," she said, perking up a little. "I can't wait. How does anyone wait?"

"No choice unless you've got a hidden zipper," Sydney cracked. The tension and fatigue were affecting him in the opposite way from Bonnie. He seemed giddy and restless.

"Mother told Syd I would have my baby at five A.M. That's when I was born," Bonnie said. She looked at me. "You know, Mom's really okay. It's just that she still thinks of me as a little girl. I don't think she's adjusted to my being married yet."

"She'd better hurry up," Sydney said, "or you know what that makes our baby."

Bonnie glared at him. "Don't joke about our baby. Joke about it after it's born. Not now."

"Did you deliver your own children, Dr. Sweeney?" Sydney changed the subject quickly.

"No," I said. "I've known obstetricians who have, but I wouldn't want to. Because I'm no longer a doctor then. I'm too emotionally involved to think the way I should. I don't take care of anybody in my family."

"I guess you watched your children being born, though," Sydney said.

"I was in the labor room but I didn't go into the delivery room." Bonnie and Sydney looked surprised. "It's different when Sydney comes in with you, because he's not a doctor. Having a husband there who is a doctor puts an awful lot of pressure on the guy who's doing the delivery. And it wouldn't have been fair to my wife, either. There was enough pressure on her already because she was Dr. Sweeney's wife in labor. She would really have had to act like the exemplary mother-to-be if I were present." And I thought to myself, "Besides, how could I stand there if anything was going wrong? Knowing as much as I do, I couldn't possibly be there."

Bonnie's contractions were coming every couple of minutes now, and conversation was sporadic. After one contraction I said, "You two know your baby is a couple of weeks late —what we call a postmature baby. So don't be surprised if it looks like a little old man. It will be wrinkled, and the skin will be coarser or maybe scaly at first. It's as if you stayed in a bathtub of salty water for too long."

Bonnie thought this over. "Does it go away soon?"

I told her the baby would gain weight and the wrinkles would disappear. They are there in the first place because this baby hasn't been adding fat during the last couple of weeks in the uterus.

"Thanks for telling us," Bonnie said. She settled back quietly for a while.

At 2:45 A.M. we wheeled Bonnie into the delivery room, with Sydney walking alongside. The excitement of the move banished Bonnie's fatigue. When we transferred her to the delivery table, the first thing she wanted was to have the mirror adjusted so she could see everything.

"It should be larger," she said, surveying her surroundings. "If you were where I am, you'd see that the mirror is too small."

Bonnie seemed so strong and in such good spirits that in

all fairness, I couldn't help thinking Mrs. Garfinkel must have done something right.

We waited a while in the delivery room, which is unusual. But we had taken Bonnie down a little early because the floor had been so quiet. Generally things move fast in there. Ladies sometimes ask me, "How come they leave you for hours in the labor room and then suddenly you're rushed to delivery and everyone is dashing around like mad as if they had no warning of what was going to happen?" I guess that's how it seems, but actually we just don't want to take up the room until the lady's ready to give birth. Someone else might need it.

I was still waiting for caput, and trying to get Bonnie to bear down with the contractions. One trouble with the epidural is that since the woman hardly feels any pain, she doesn't push. And her muscle power is greatly reduced, so the incidence of low-forceps deliveries is increased. Often we have to pull the baby out. But it's a very simple little operation because everything's so relaxed. Doing it doesn't bother me at all.

Finally we had caput. The nurse prepped Bonnie, washing her with disinfectant, while I scrubbed with Dr. Richards, the resident.

"She's got an epidural," I told him, "but her contractions have been pretty good."

We went back in. Bonnie was tense and excited. The baby's head was down against the vaginal opening. When the fundus nurse felt the uterus contract she nodded at me and I said, "Push *now*, Bonnie. Try to push down."

She tried. "There's an awful lot of *pressure*," she gasped.

"Don't raise your hips," I said.

"Aaah." Bonnie exhaled the exclamation. "I feel as if I'm splitting." She panted. "It's not real pain, but I can't believe the pressure."

"Push again, honey. As hard as you can."

She did, staring in the mirror as she strained. "My God," she blurted, "I think I saw the top of the head! Was that the baby's head?"

"Yes."

"It went back *in*."

"I know. That's perfectly normal."

Suddenly she said, "I'm scared, Dr. Sweeney."

"Everything's fine, Bonnie. Just fine."

She was quiet, frightened. She tried to bear down when I told her to, but the baby didn't move. The widest part of its head wasn't coming out.

"I'm going to put on the forceps to help the baby's head come out, Bonnie." I wondered whether the mirror was such a good idea after all. "Why don't you stop looking for a minute."

"It's okay," she whispered. "I want to see."

The baby's head was down low, and the forceps went on easily. I locked them and sat down. Most people stand up to deliver. That's what I was taught. But I think I'm more in control of the forces of labor when I'm sitting. Besides, that way I can't drop the baby. Newborn infants are slippery and sometimes squirming. If I'm sitting down, I know at worst the baby will fall in my lap.

I pulled gently against the forceps handles. The head moved down, and I released. Then I pulled again, holding the head against the vagina, which was relaxed and stretching enormously as it does.

"Bonnie," I said, "I'm going to cut the episiotomy, and it's not the prettiest thing in the world. Why don't you close your eyes for a minute. There'll be some blood."

"I want to see," she said stubbornly.

The epidural had made a local anesthetic unnecessary. I held the forceps with my left hand and when Dr. Richards handed me the scissors, I cut the episiotomy. A crimson spurt of blood ran down onto the drapes beneath Bonnie's buttocks. Bonnie gasped. I increased traction on the forceps. The pressure slowed the bleeding, and the baby's head moved down. I eased up and pulled again. Then I took the forceps off and had the baby's face in my hands. We went ahead and delivered her baby with Bonnie and Sydney watching and momentary silence in the room. "Oh my God, it's out, it's out," Bonnie cried as his trunk came down and I grabbed his legs. "Is it all right? I can't see anything."

"He's in my *lap*," I said, sucking out the mucus with a bulb syringe, "and you've got a boy."

Sydney was standing next to me and he said, "Sweetheart, he's *beautiful*."

Bonnie started crying a split second before the baby started screaming.

"Is he really all right?" she sobbed.

"He's fine, Bonnie. Congratulations, both of you." I was holding the baby in my lap below the level of the placenta to allow him to get as much blood as possible before I clamped the cord.

Bonnie was still crying and blinking through her tears at the mirror when I said, "You can stop looking up there, he's *here*!" I was at her side holding the baby for her to see. He was really howling.

Bonnie sobbed, "Oh, Sydney, he's wonderful, isn't he beautiful?"

He was all wrinkled and he did look like a tiny old man, but he was a good little boy and to the Levys the most gorgeous baby in the world.

"He has such tiny, perfect fingers," Bonnie whispered, smiling tearily with a kind of bliss these mothers feel.

I placed the little boy on Bonnie's stomach. All she said was "Oh." Sydney touched the baby's shoulder and kissed Bonnie.

"I love you," Bonnie told him. He began crying and that started Bonnie again. "Thank you, Dr. Sweeney," Bonnie sobbed. "He's perfect. It was all so perfect we should have taken pictures."

Sydney kissed her forehead. "You're crazy and beautiful and I love you."

"I'm so happy," Bonnie sobbed. "I love everyone. There's only one thing wrong. I can never have another first baby."

13. Operation

Mavis Rogers finally agreed to be operated on. Big, stubborn red-haired Mavis, who had refused for over a year to have her ovaries out, suddenly changed her mind. My office mail arrived one day with a large envelope from her containing a drawing made by her older daughter, Nina. It was a big crayon heart with handmade paper flowers taped around it and "Love to Mommy and Daddy" written in the center. Attached was a note from Mavis:

Dear Dr. S.:
Nina gave us this today after her tenth birthday party and said, "Parents should get presents too because children couldn't have birthdays without them." When do you want to operate?
Mavis

We scheduled her for two weeks later, on July 1. The hospital gave me an 8 A.M. operating time, which I like so I won't have to follow anybody. Otherwise I can never be sure how long the surgeon ahead of me is going to take. But the night before Mavis's operation, I was up until 4 A.M. delivering

Bonnie Levy, and I told myself again that I couldn't go on at this pace. It's not right to go into an operation without enough sleep, although I forget I'm tired once I'm there. On top of everything, I had a summer cold, and they're the worst ones to get rid of.

I was doing a bilateral oophorectomy on Mavis. The medical terms sound impersonal and fine. But it's not so nice to do a bilateral castration, and that's what this operation is. I don't think many male gynecologists would like to be castrated at the age of thirty-five. The fact that testicles hang outside the body doesn't make them any different from ovaries. I have to make an incision to get to the ovaries, but I'm still castrating this lady. I think the only reason that removing a woman's ovaries is considered less serious psychologically than castrating a man is male chauvinism. That's it, right there. Otherwise there are not many differences. You don't need testicles for intercourse any more than you need ovaries. A eunuch, for example, can have intercourse; he just can't get anybody pregnant, which is why they had them guarding the harems. They weren't worried about screwing, they were worried about giving the sultan or whoever it was an illegitimate heir. Little boys can get erections and they could have intercourse if they knew what it was all about, even though they might not yet be producing testosterone, or the male hormone.

An oophorectomy is traumatic for any woman, but especially if she's young. Mavis was frightened to death about what this would do to her; what physiological changes it would cause. Well, we can take care of most of those changes with hormones. But psychologically, she was losing her womanhood, and that's a terrible thing to face. I guess she'd still be refusing if she weren't thinking first about her kids. She asked me the same question most ladies ask: whether removing the ovaries would stop her sex drive. It won't. Physiologically, that is. But psychologically it might, unless she gets some help. Just as removing the testicles might so damage a man's confidence in his masculinity that his sex drive would be impaired.

Medically, the question of when to take out a woman's ovaries is a problem. With Mavis, where the indications to operate were so strong, the answer was evident. Similarly, if we're performing a hysterectomy on a sixty-five-year-old woman whose ovaries are no longer functioning and who has a great chance of getting cancer in them, we'll take them out. But what about the forty-year-old woman who has a benign tumor of the uterus? We'll take out the uterus because we don't want to leave in an organ that has a strong cancer potential. She's not planning to have any more kids anyway. But what do we do about her ovaries, which are normal and may have ten or fifteen years of function left in them?

We've got to establish our own guide lines or we'll drive ourselves and the women crazy. When I was on the hospital staff, the policy, as I remember it, was, in women between forty and forty-five, leave the ovaries in; between forty-five and fifty, take out one; and over fifty, remove both. A student once asked me, "Why? Why do you leave *one* in? It doesn't make any sense."

And it doesn't. Taking out one ovary doesn't cut the chance of cancer in half. Suppose I decide, "Okay, I've had four women who have developed cancer of the left ovary. Therefore in patients over forty-five, I will take out all left ovaries and leave in all right ones." And the next four women have cancer of the right ovary. No. Either we have indications to take them both out or we should leave them both in. I think that after the age of fifty, whenever major abdominal surgery is being done anyway, both ovaries should be removed. Before fifty, they should be left in. If another surgeon picks forty-five as his age limit, I can't argue with him. That's his belief. Whatever age limit we set, we're all going to have the patient who develops cancer of those ovaries we left in.

Then we kick ourselves around the block for that woman we could have saved.

When Mavis finally agreed to the operation, she knew it included a hysterectomy: there was no reason to leave in the uterus, which is a cancer-prone organ. I was just hoping we wouldn't find the beginning of anything. When I stopped to see Mavis the night before her surgery, she said, "I think I'm having psychosomatic symptoms, doc. My stomach has felt a little bloated for the past couple of days."

It was the first time she'd mentioned this and I was shocked. I thought, "It *must* be psychosomatic. If she's really feeling anything, we're already too late."

A few minutes before 8 A.M., I was in the locker room pulling a green scrub suit over my underwear. The scrub suit is a pair of pants and a short-sleeved jacket that's been laundered but not ironed, so it's rumpled-looking. A lot of people see us around the hospital in these outfits and think we're janitors. Then I put on the disposable paper shoe covers we wear over our street shoes. The covers are clean and they are grounded with a strip of rubber-encased metal that slips inside each shoe against the soles of our feet. We're using explosive gases in the anesthesia, and a spark could blow up the whole operating room. It's happened.

While I was still outside the operating room, I put on my hat and mask. We just got special hats that look more like hoods for the doctors with long hair or beards, but I don't need one of those. Our masks have a band of pliable plastic across the top. I can pinch it to make the mask conform over the bridge of my nose. Since I wear glasses when I operate, I'm pretty careful about getting the mask fitted tightly so it won't obscure my vision.

I walked into the operating room and checked the X-rays of Mavis's pelvis, which were clipped to a light box on the wall. Dr. Davis, the senior resident who was assisting me, was

already scrubbed. Mavis was on the table and the rest of the
team was in the room. There were five besides Dr. Davis and
me: the anesthesiologist, who was seated and talking to an
intern at the head of the table; another intern who was
scrubbed and ready to stand at the table with us; the scrub
nurse, who was scrubbed and sterile and would handle the
instruments and sutures; and the circulating nurse, who was
not sterile. She wore a scrub dress, mask and hat, but no
gown or gloves, and she could touch things that weren't sterile. If we dropped a pair of scissors we were going to need,
this circulating nurse could pick them up and take them out
to be sterilized. If we needed blood, she would call for it. Or
she could call my office and tell them I was going to be late
—again.

I knew this team of nurses—they were assigned just to the
GYN operating room—and they were good, and nice besides.
The surgical nurses rotate: one day one is scrubbed, the other
circulates; then they switch. This morning Miss Snow, the
scrub nurse, was standing at her tray cutting sutures to the
right length, threading them into the curved needles we
would be using, and then laying them out carefully and fold-
ing them between sterile towels. And she and the circulating
nurse were checking everything. All through the operation,
every item is counted. When we finish, the nurses have to
have the same number of instruments, sponges and lap pads,
or sterile absorbent cloths, they came in with. You've never
seen such a turmoil as when we're about to close and a nurse
says, "We're missing a Kelly clamp." We have to find it. Most
times, thank God, it's a miscount. Or the turmoil if we break
a needle. We use a new needle and suture for each stitch, so
if I hand the needle back to the nurse and she says, "This is
only half of it, where's the other half?" I've got to find it. Or
if we lose a sponge or lap pad, it's got to be accounted for.
Otherwise it's in the patient, presumably. Of course, it's
usually *not*. But there are times the nurses have to search the

operating room floor, the table and all through the folds of the drapes or sterile sheets covering the patient. It's possible to leave a sponge or lap pad inside the patient, and that's a malpractice suit right there. The hell with the suit, think of the harm to the patient.

I went out to scrub in the small area adjacent to the operating room. The scrub sink is like a little bathtub suspended from the wall, and the hot and cold water operate with foot pedals. I learned to scrub in the '49 drought, so I don't run the water all the time. Today we only have to do a three- to five-minute scrub, but it's a very thorough one, and all surgeons have red dishpan-looking hands. We scrub with brushes or rough disposable pads and pHisoHex or some other disinfectant. We use a disposable wood stick to clean under our nails. There's a definite technique to scrubbing, so when you see those doctors on TV walking around with their hands up in front of their faces and the water running down off their elbows, they're not playing games. What we do is scrub halfway up our arms, which is why our scrub suits are short-sleeved. Then we wash the disinfectant off with our hands held up, so the water runs down to our elbows or upper arms, which haven't been scrubbed. It wouldn't do any good to scrub and then lower our hands, letting dirty water run over them.

Once a surgeon's scrubbed, that's it. He doesn't touch anything. I walked into the operating room with my hands up, pushing the swinging doors open with my shoulder. Using a pair of tongs, the nurse gave me a sterile towel and I dried. Again, we dry in a special way so that we won't contaminate anything. Then she held up a sterile green gown and I put my arms into the sleeves, which are tight around the wrists like those of a ski jacket. The circulating nurse tied the back for me. From then on, nobody could touch that gown in front, because it was sterile. Sometimes we'll be operating and get an itch that drives us crazy. We can't scratch. If it's in a nonvital spot, like my back, I can get the nurse to come over and scratch me if I want. Or if my chest itches, I can scratch it with sterile gloves through the sterile gown. But if the itch is someplace I can't ask a nurse to scratch, I just suffer.

There are two ways to put gloves on. The better method is with the glove already in place around the wrist of the gown, so my hand comes down through the sleeve and right into the glove without ever being exposed. But that "closed" technique is newer and a little more difficult, so not many places employ it. Before Mavis's operation, I used the familiar open technique, plunging my hand into the glove Miss Snow was holding and feeling my fingers go all the way down as the wrist of the glove snapped tight over my sleeve and wrist. These gloves are like a second skin. I can feel everything when I'm wearing them, and even see the hair on the back of my hand.

Mavis was covered except for her abdomen, which had been scrubbed and disinfected. Dr. Davis said, "Vertical incision all right?" I said yes, and he painted a line on her skin as I walked over to the table. A couple of students were upstairs in the observation room. At a teaching institution, there are always people coming to watch. If they've got scrub suits and masks on, they can actually stand inside the operating room and look over my shoulder as long as they don't touch anything. I invite students into my operating room to observe, learn, question and grow. Only when an acute emergency arises are they asked to step away and be quiet. Even then, they're learning what it means to be a surgeon.

There was a moment of silence, everyone settling into the tremendous concentration and alertness that takes over the operating room. Nothing else in the world exists from now on. We're isolated from everything except what's directly in front of us.

"Are we ready?" I was standing on Mavis's left side. I

glanced at the anesthesiologist seated behind the head of the table. He nodded, checking his instruments. Mavis was anesthetized and *paralyzed,* which is something they do with the anesthesia to relax all the muscles and keep the patient absolutely motionless. She couldn't breathe while she was that way, so the anesthesiologist was breathing for her, his hand squeezing the black bag which was hooked up to the anesthesia machine. The instruments on the machine controlled the pressure and mix of oxygen and anesthetic. A tube was taped into Mavis's mouth, going down into her trachea and taking the mixture to her lungs.

"Okay, let's go to work," I said.

I held out my right hand. Miss Snow put the scalpel into it, handle flat against my palm. I made the initial incision, tracing over the painted line on the abdominal skin. Not very deep, just through the skin and subcutaneous fat situated under the skin. A thin red line of blood appeared in the wake of the knife. The nurse gave me another knife, since the one used to cut through the skin was no longer considered sterile. I traced over the initial incision again, a little deeper. Stop then and look for bleeders, or little blood vessels, pick up each one, clamp it off and tie it. Mavis was stout—a lot of abdominal fat—and the fat popped out and pushed the incision apart so it bulged a little.

Gradually I cut deeper, going over the same line, each time stopping to pick up and tie off the bleeders. Across the table from me, Dr. Davis picked up the little blood vessels he had a better angle on. The intern sponged away some blood. The scrub nurse handed us clamps, sutures, sponges as needed. I didn't look up. A good surgeon never turns away from the field. He just holds out his hand and the nurse puts what he needs into it. Without nurses, we couldn't work. I think the scrub nurse has the toughest job at the whole table because she must anticipate what we want; but usually she is so good we don't have to say a word.

We went slowly and carefully through all the layers of fat. Sometimes we wonder if we're ever going to get down through it, and we hate a fat lady at this point. Her stoutness makes the operation more difficult and the healing slower. I had started at five past eight. Dr. Davis said, "Eight-thirty and we're not in yet."

Past the fat finally, we reached a strong layer of connective tissue called fascia that supports and binds together the internal organs. Cut through that and we saw the peritoneum, or membrane that encloses the abdominal cavity. *Peritoneum* comes from the Greek, meaning "stretched over." An incision through this translucent membrane and finally we were in the peritoneal cavity.

Miss Snow handed the intern a McBurney retractor, which is a metal pulling instrument that looks like a little hoe. He positioned it in one side of the incision, then placed a second retractor on the opposite side and held the incision open.

We saw then a dark hole with loops of bowel, which are pinkish-bluish. The pelvic ligaments were glistening. The uterus looked like an inverted, flattened pear, ovaries like two wrinkled whitish walnuts and fallopian tubes like narrow pink or reddish trumpets flaring open at each end. They're attached to either side of the uterus and go horizontally across the abdominal cavity, so the uterus seems to be suspended from them.

Of course, what it looks like in the abdominal cavity depends on what we're in there for. The uterus doesn't look pearlike if it's all distorted with tumors, and the ovaries may be hidden with cysts twining around them. There was no odor that morning, but sometimes the smell is overwhelming when an infected cavity is opened.

"Let's look around," I said. Theoretically, I could have done this whole thing vaginally—remove everything through the vagina—instead of going into the abdomen. It would have made the postoperative course a lot easier, but that way

I wouldn't have had the opportunity to investigate the entire abdominal cavity. If I had been doing a vaginal hysterectomy for benign fibroid tumors, I might not have needed to look around. But Mavis came from a family full of ovarian cancer. Suddenly Mavis strained and the intestines, like a bowl of spaghetti brimming over, filled and ran over my incision.

"Goddamit now, Mort, keep her asleep!" I snapped at the anesthesiologist.

He adjusted two dials on his machine and mumbled something I didn't hear. Anesthesiologists are a funny bunch. I'll say to them, "Why can't you do this right? Nurses give this." And they'll come right back at me: "Cops deliver babies!" But anesthesiology is a tough job and a great responsibility. That's why I would like to select the anesthesiologist for my patient as carefully as I would for my family. Any time a person goes to sleep under anesthesia there's the risk he may not wake up. So when people ask me, "Is it a minor procedure?" I always think of that.

I started going over everything in the abdominal cavity, talking aloud to Dr. Davis for my own benefit and his, and for everyone in the operating and observation rooms. "Upper abdominal cavity feels good; no fluid, everything's clean." I reached across, felt and turned the right ovary, which was farthest from me. "Right ovary normal, firm." I came back to the ovary closest to me. "Left ovary—" I stopped. "Left ovary appears enlarged—nodular and gritty on the underneath surface." I felt a surge of anger as I described what we call neoplastic seeding, the earliest sign of possible ovarian cancer. If the carcinoma is more advanced, the ovaries are studded with smallish white lumps. They look like those old-fashioned balls of caramel popcorn.

"I'll want a frozen section," I said, my voice sounding hard and cold as I tried to control my anger at this lousy disease.

The circulating nurse went to the wall intercom and called the Pathology Lab.

"Pathology Lab." The response came loud and clear.

"This is Dr. Sweeney in the GYN operating room." I remained at the operating table. The intercom would pick up my voice across the room. "I've got a thirty-five-year-old lady here with a very strong family history of ovarian carcinoma. Her left ovary looks a little suspicious and I'd like a frozen section."

"Send it right over." The lab switched off.

"Goddamit," I said to no one in particular, "she's been putting this off for a year. I couldn't get her in." I was still examining. "Uterus is negative." I felt the liver and looked at the peritoneum and intestines. Nothing. "She told me last night her stomach had been feeling full but there's nothing here she could have *felt,* not yet."

"She probably just had pre-op jitters," Dr. Davis said.

I was going over the omentum, which is a fat pad in the abdomen that has a tendency to pick up ovarian cells like a scavenger—one of the first places ovarian carcinoma spreads to. "It looks clean, but if the ovary is positive, we'll take it out," I muttered. "I need another mask, and then let's get this done." I often chew through a mask when I'm operating, because of the tension.

The circulating nurse got a second mask and replaced mine. "I thought you sounded as if you had a cold, Dr. Sweeney."

I didn't answer her. "Okay, let's get the ovaries and uterus out."

I grasped the two ligaments that hold up the uterus, severed each and ligated, or tied, what I'd cut with some catgut sutures. Then I made an incision across the front of the uterus to get the bladder out of the way. Two ligaments contain the vessels that bring the blood supply into the ovaries. We doubly clamped and cut the one to the right ovary, ligated the stump and dropped it back in. You can't just remove an organ without taking out the blood supply first.

We severed the corresponding ligament to the left ovary. Now we had taken the blood supply of both ovaries and were committed as far as they were concerned.

I made an incision across the back of the uterus and pushed the rectum out of the way. The blood supply of the uterus was coming up from each side in the uterine vessels, so we clamped, cut and ligated them. Now the main blood supply to the uterus and ovaries was gone. Next I was going to get the cervix, which is all part of the same organ. I went down and clamped the cardinal ligaments alongside of the cervix and cut them. I made an anterior incision into the vagina and cut right around to free the cervix.

"Where's the tray?"

Miss Snow as always was at my elbow, holding the oblong metal pan. I reached into the abdomen, lifted everything out at once and dropped it all in the tray. The ovaries were still attached to the uterus by the ovarian ligaments. I took another knife, cut the left ovary free and put it in a smaller tray. The ovary was handed to the circulating nurse, who quickly wrapped it in waxed paper, labeled it and gave it to an orderly to take downstairs to the Pathology Lab. The lab would deep-freeze the tissue and make a slide of it, which they could stain and examine immediately.

And I was angry, hating the uncertainty, hating the possibility of carcinoma when I hadn't expected anything.

"Okay, let's close the vagina while we're waiting." The top of the vagina where I had cut out the cervix was open and we had to sew it up because you can't leave a hole there. Then I put the cardinal ligaments that had been supporting the uterus back on the sides of the vagina to hold it up.

No word from the Path Lab. I knew the pathologists were working as quickly as they could, but when you are in the operating room waiting, it seems like an eternity until they give you the answer.

"Do we have any P-32 tubes in here?" I asked.

"I'll get some." The circulating nurse left.

"I need to change masks again," I said. Damn cold. God forbid I should sneeze in the middle of a delicate procedure.

Everyone in the room snapped to attention as the pathologist's voice came over the intercom. "Dr. Sweeney?"

"Yes."

"The ovary looks suspicious, but it's going to take more sections with special stains to give you a final diagnosis. We just can't tell you today."

"Okay. Thanks." The anger was suddenly gone.

I requested clamps to proceed with the removal of the omentum. As we worked, Dr. Davis asked, "Are you going to put in the tubes anyway?"

"Yeah, even if it's just a precaution, I'd rather do it than not. It'll scare her when she wakes up and finds them, but there's no other way that's safe."

The P-32 tubes are left inside the patient, protruding from the wound so that when we've finished, we can instill radioactive phosphorus into the peritoneal cavity. We only do this when there is a minimal amount of ovarian carcinoma. The phosphorus, although it's radioactive, is a beta-ray emitter, different from radium and X-ray, which emit gamma rays. With phosphorus the effect of the radiation is limited to a depth of only two or three millimeters. If the disease is too widespread or thick, this procedure is insufficient. But in a case like Mavis's, we can put the phosphorus in postoperatively, mixed with some fluid so it will slosh around inside and deliver radiation to the whole of the abdomen.

At this point we were ready to close, which meant putting back all the layers we had opened. After working for a while, I told Dr. Davis to do some of the sewing. He's already a pretty good surgeon. Once I said, "Better put one or two more sutures in there," and the rest of the time I just watched.

Usually when we're closing, a certain amount of the pressure is off. Not that we relax. We've still got a patient under anesthesia and we want to finish and get her into recovery. But if everything has gone well, we talk about different things while we're sewing away. As we worked on Mavis, there were a couple of comments about the coming July Fourth weekend and who was going to do what, but I didn't feel like joining in, and the others must have noticed my reserve. It was a pretty quiet closing.

Two days later I stopped at the Pathology Lab for the second time. The report on Mavis was ready to be sent up to the floor where her room was. The capital letters after the word *Diagnosis* jumped out at me: EARLY ADENOCAR-CINOMA OF THE OVARY. I looked at the slide. I felt sure we had gotten to Mavis in time, but staring at the tell-tale undisciplined cell changes which indicate malignancy, I shivered and thought, "We were lucky on this one. Another couple of months and we would have had to remove everything in sight."

14. "Dr. Sweeney"

After finishing Mavis's operation, which had taken two and a half hours, I talked to her husband, who was waiting for me in her room. Then I dictated my operative notes into the central tape recorder at the hospital, where somebody would pick them off the tape and type them. I like to do this as soon as possible so I remember all the details, but if I don't have time there, I can dictate from my office on our hospital line, which can be plugged directly into the dictating room. I left the hospital making quick rounds on my way out.

I'm always keyed up after an operation, just as I used to be each time I played a football game. I'm more affected after a cancer case, so when I got to the office around 11:15 A.M., the fatigue still hadn't hit me. Thursdays are supposed to be my free mornings. If I don't have to operate, I usually go over lab reports, dictate letters, write my papers, read journals or prepare a lecture. Anyway, patients don't start until noon. I thought I'd get everything I could out of the way, including last night's phone calls, so I could leave on time for a change—but that's not how the next forty-five minutes worked out.

First, I got conned into returning a call from an insurance agent. Sometimes they'll phone and not tell Mrs. Donohue what they want because they know they won't get through. So they just leave a message that Dr. Sweeney should call Mr. Blankety Blank at such-and-such a number. Well, I didn't know who Mr. Blankety Blank was. I called him back and the next minute he was trying to sell me extra insurance for the equipment in my office. It was a short conversation because I've got plenty of insurance as it is. But a couple of minutes later, the doorbell rang. Our office door is kept locked when I'm here alone. I certainly wasn't expecting any patients, but it could have been an emergency, so I went out front and said, "Who is it?"

A woman's voice gave me a name and said, "I'm here to see Dr. Sweeney."

I thought, "It must be a patient who made a mistake." I opened the door and there stood a well-groomed businesslike woman, with a sample case. She walked in and set the case on Katey's desk and I thought, "Oh my God, now I've been ambushed by a detail man, only he's female!"

And sure enough, she was from one of the drug companies. I guess it's another place where Women's Lib has caught on. Each drug company sends detail men around trying to sell the doctor its new products. I don't like to turn them away —they're doing their job, too, and they might even have something I want to hear about. But I can't possibly see them all, so either Katey lets them in at certain times, maybe at lunch if I'm having a bowl of soup at the desk, or she takes a sample and a brochure.

I listened to this woman for a minute, took something, thanked her and she left.

I was just putting the sample on top of the bundle of mail I'd picked up by the office door when I noticed the top envelope right under the string. It was pale blue and marked "Personal" above my name. I slipped it out, opened it, and looked at the signature first. It was from Mrs. Elise Fremont. After a minute I placed the name: the French lady with the suntan. The writing was elegant and the note was short and to the point: she had enjoyed meeting me and would like to see me outside of the office. I could reach her at the Regency Hotel until July 23, and if she didn't hear from me, she would assume I was not interested and wouldn't bother me again.

Now, if I'm going to be honest, this sort of thing is flattering. I've sometimes thought women were telling me about their affairs to see if they could add me to their list, but I'd never been asked before in writing. I didn't think less of her for having written it, although I guess I'm still a little surprised at the amount of infidelity that's going on. I wish I'd known about this in high school; things would have been different. But I wasn't interested, and I tore Mrs. Fremont's letter into several pieces and dropped them in the wastebasket.

I went back into my office and returned a few more calls. Halfway through the stack was another man's name, and I thought, "I've had my booby traps for the day. This one's got to be legitimate." I phoned and by God, it was a man who wanted to sell me alarm switches that could be hidden under the desks. I told him we already had them—which we do: we have one alarm system in case somebody tries to break in and burglarize the office when it's locked, and another system we can set off secretly in case somebody walks into this place full of women and tries any funny stuff. And then I gave up. I locked the office and went up to the corner restaurant, had some orange juice for my cold and a hamburger for lunch. When I came back, the girls were in and office hours started.

Betsy Merrill, my shiny, brown-haired little girl who'd been having artificial insemination with her husband's sperm, was pregnant. The AIH we'd done in May had worked, and she was about the happiest girl I knew. She kept kidding me about how she'd been sure all along; how I might be the big obstetrician-gynecologist, but I didn't know a thing concerning the way a woman could *feel* that she was pregnant.

When Katey brought in my afternoon list and I saw Betsy's name at the top, I grinned. "Nice way to start off the day."

Katey gave me one of her business looks. "Dr. Sweeney, I've got a feeling I'd better remind you that you've made the decision to give *up* obstetrics. It's taken us a year to get the number of patients on our books down to where they are, and Mrs. Merrill's not due until February."

"Yeah, I know. It's just that I'd really like to deliver this one."

"You'd really like to deliver them all if you could," Katey commented.

"Okay! Now stop bossing me around. This is my office. Isn't it my office?"

She nodded calmly. "How long are we going to keep Mrs. Merrill before you turn her over?"

"Until her fifth month." If, God forbid, she was going to have any problems or a miscarriage in her early pregnancy, I thought it was only fair that she should have them with me.

Katey left and I went in to see Betsy. Laura had already taken her blood pressure, and Betsy was sitting on the edge of the table grinning from ear to ear.

"I don't think I have to ask how you are," I said.

"Dr. Sweeney, would you believe it if I told you I can feel it growing?"

"Sure. Want to skip the examination?"

Betsy went down on the table so fast that Laura laughed.

"Not on your life," she said. "Take a good look, please, because then I want to know what Alex and I can do on our vacation."

I examined her and everything was fine. A few minutes later in my consultation room, I told her she could do anything she felt like, only not to exert herself when she was tired.

"Betsy," I said then, "I told you before but I want to remind you—I won't be delivering your baby."

Her face fell. "I know. I've just tried not to think about that. I thought maybe—maybe something would happen and you'd change your mind."

"I'm sorry, honey. If I was going to deliver anyone, it would be you, but I'm just not delivering any ladies after December."

"I understand. And I'm glad you'll be doing what you want. It's just that—" She was staring at me and those big brown eyes were filling with tears.

"Come on, now, Betsy," I said. "I'll be seeing you for another few months."

She nodded, blinking hard.

"If you like, I can suggest another obstetrician when it's time to switch. He's a very good man, and he's kind and I think you'll like him a lot."

"Okay," she whispered, "but he won't be you. This baby —you gave Alex and me our baby." And the tears spilled over. "I just can't imagine somebody else delivering him." She wiped her cheeks with the back of her hand.

"Don't worry, Betsy. It will all work out. Now you and Alex go have a good vacation."

"Thank you, Dr. Sweeney. I know we will." She tried a smile. "We're both so happy."

I came from behind the desk and walked her to the door with my arm around her shoulders. "You okay?"

"Sure." Her eyes were brimming. "Can I just go into the bathroom for a minute?"

Katey told me later that she cried her head off in there, then came out very calm and made her next appointment.

Seven and a half months later, when I was no longer doing

obstetrics, I well remember the morning in February when I went to the hospital. I didn't have an operation, but I hit the floor at 8 A.M. and looked up on the board and there she was: Mrs. Alex Merrill. Betsy was not only in labor, she was in the delivery room.

I hadn't seen her since she switched to Dr. Abrams, but I'd gotten a Christmas card from her and Alex saying all was well. So I ran down to the room still dressed in my street clothes and I stuck my head in the door and said, "See, I told you I wouldn't miss your delivery!"

Betsy was lying on the table with her back to me—Alex was in there too—and she said, "It's Dr. Sweeney, it's Dr. Sweeney!" without even looking around.

So I ran and got into my scrub suit and went roaring back to the delivery room, and Ben Abrams said, "Do you want to deliver her?"

"Yeah, sure I want to deliver her," I said, "but no—I sent her to you. Go ahead."

And then I stood there while she was delivered. They had a beautiful little girl, and Betsy was crying and saying, "Oh, thank you God, thank you God." Alex was crying, too, and I was bawling myself. That old feeling was still there. The practice of obstetrics has more fun and happiness than anything else you do. And standing there watching these kids who finally got their baby, I thought, "I've got to get out of here or I'll go back into business."

It was a terribly hard thing, phasing out of obstetrics. The problem was that my kind of gynecology involved a lot of cancer surgery, and I couldn't schedule a cancer case that might take four or eight hours and then be up the whole night before delivering a baby. That wasn't fair to the patient in the operating room, so when the gynecology built up to the point where I couldn't do justice to both, something had to go.

At first I thought, "I'll *limit* my obstetrics, but I'm not going to give it up. I'll keep, say, ten obstetrical ladies on my books, and see and deliver them." Well, you can't do that because the eleventh lady is the one you delivered three times before, and you can't say no to her; and then the twelfth one comes in and says, "But you're delivering my sister, why won't you deliver me?" So you never give up at that rate.

Then I thought, "I'll limit my practice by charging more. That'll do it. If they can't afford to come, they won't." First we doubled my fee. Katey came in after six months of that and said, "You've only lost one patient." So then we raised the fee again, but we still had too many women on our obstetrical list. And I thought, "This is just not what I want to do. I want to limit the number of patients I'm delivering, not keep on with nearly the same number and double the money." So finally I just said no to everybody. And it was terribly difficult. Everyone had the same story: "Oh, I'm so glad you're quitting obstetrics, you're so tired, but you'll take care of *me*." But we stuck to it. I still accepted infertility patients, but I warned them I couldn't deliver them.

As young doctors, almost all of us start out doing a lot of obstetrics. A woman doesn't want to be operated on by a guy who looks like he's just gotten out of the Boy Scouts, but she'll have a baby with a man who looks like he's no older. Besides, even with the birth rate dropping, there are a heck of a lot more babies being born than there are operations being done. So at first it's primarily an obstetrical practice. And it builds through the patients: one woman likes me and she tells the next pregnant woman and she tells the next and off I go.

Then we grow older—and our patients do. There's a well-known dictum that the obstetrician delivers babies and then becomes a gynecologist and repairs all the mistakes he made as an obstetrician. Eventually most of us tend to specialize one way or another. We get to be known for what we're doing primarily, and the practice in that area builds faster. Finally, if you're a gynecological surgeon and faced with a conflict, you have to make a decision.

Fran was glad I was getting out of obstetrics. I guess when I thought about quitting that business, her feelings were certainly one factor I considered. They either make you or break you, those women at home. If they're understanding, it's just great. But how understanding can a wife be after a while? It must be awful. We go to a party and there's a room filled with people standing around laughing and talking and drinking. And the phone rings. Four or five heads look up: they're the four or five doctors at the party. Hardly anyone else even hears the phone. We do, and we know one of us will be called. And look at the five wives and watch their faces fall: they know one of them is going home again.

We live by the phone and the beeper, and we get to hate phones. Our wives get to hate them, too. At home I jump a foot every time the phone rings, even if the phone is part of a television program. I go away for a vacation. I'm off on some island down in the Caribbean, and for the first week, every time the phone rings, I still jump.

Do you know how many telephones there are in Broadway theaters? You don't know, but we do. One phone in each. I didn't realize that plays on Broadway had three acts until I started quitting obstetrics. They've got three whole acts! The people pour out afterward and it's just tremendous to be part of that mob for a change. You see, an obstetrician doesn't just miss the third act because he gets called away. He misses the end of every act because if he waited until intermission to call his service or the hospital, he wouldn't even get to the phone. He'd end up standing outside the booth while some jerk sat in there telling his friend about the play, or some daddy called to see if the baby-sitter was awake.

When my wife and I go to a movie and I don't want to take the beeper because it makes such a racket, I tell the service what theater we're going to. I hand the theater manager my card and say, "If I get called, this is my name." Then he makes us sit where he wants to put us: right on the aisle, so he can quietly find me if he needs to. At a restaurant, I hand my card to the maître d'. He may come over during dinner just to check that everything's all right, but the minute we see him, Fran and I are braced for a medical call. Most people outside the profession don't know about this stuff, but a doctor's wife and kids do. When my own boys were young and I took them to a football game, I would either have to take another adult along to stay with them in case I had to leave, or I'd have to drag them, complaining unhappily, from the game.

Of course getting out of obstetrics doesn't mean eliminating emergency calls. There is still the woman in trouble after a botched-up abortion, the lady with a ruptured ovarian cyst or the woman with an ectopic or tubal pregnancy that ruptured. It's hard to imagine any good physician with patients who doesn't have his share of emergencies. But that's part of his business, and if he's lucky, his wife adjusts. Certainly she changes, even after a few years of marriage.

For one thing, it's assumed since her husband is a doctor that she's a medical expert. Patients will call home and ask her questions, and she gets to be a pretty good authority, as a matter of fact.

As for other aspects of married life, I guess she becomes more resigned in some ways and more resentful in others. Maybe when she got married, she had the same exalted idea of doctors as lay people have. After we've lived together for a while, though, I become a lot less exalted to her. Yet we go to a party and all she hears is how wonderful her husband is. Once in a while she'd like to hear how wonderful *she* is. But there I am, either talking shop with other doctors, or surrounded by women—still talking business.

If we are invited to a party where I'm not known, I tell the host, *"Please* don't introduce me as a doctor because that's it for the night." I'd rather tell people I'm a plumber or a golf pro. Next time you go to a party, just watch: it'll be, "I want you to meet Ed Smith and John Jones and Dr. Sweeney." This Ed Smith may be the greatest engineer in the world, and the other fellow may be a Ph.D., yet they're not introduced as that. Why can't it just be, "This is Bill Sweeney"? But a host will invariably introduce me as "doctor" and I spend the evening talking shop because I get questions. Then if they find out I'm an obstetrician and a gynecologist . . .

Not too long ago, I went home for a high school reunion. Now when I was in high school, no girl in my class would admit she had a vagina, much less let me talk about it. But there I was and everybody was drinking and having fun and I was off in a corner while my classmates told me about their menstrual periods or their friends' cramps. This happens no matter where we go.

Hell, I was in *Rome* standing at the top of the Spanish Steps and all of a sudden a voice shrieked, "Dr. Sweeney!" I thought, "Oh my God, they found me."

This woman walked over and said, "Oh, I'm so glad to see you, I wanted to ask you a few questions."

So there I stood at the top of the Spanish Steps—I could have *pushed* her *down*—and she just went ahead and asked me her few questions. On my vacation! It's fun, though. I wouldn't do anything else.

15. Abortion

On July 1, 1970, the reformed New York State abortion law went into effect, and my life has been more complicated ever since. I have conflicting feelings about abortions. On the one hand, I think every woman has the right to decide whether she wants to be pregnant, and the right to be legally aborted under good medical care. On the other hand, I don't like doing abortions, although I perform them. Recently a patient said to me, "You've probably spent too long bringing life into the world to want to end it." That sounds good, but it really isn't true. Abortion is not a moral issue for me, except possibly with a very advanced pregnancy. When I speak of not liking to do abortions, I'm talking about the actual procedure. In contrast, I'm a surgeon and I enjoy operating.

The first reason I don't like abortions is technical: it's such a blind procedure. You can't see what you're doing, and you can't really feel what you're doing. Abortion is certainly not the simple, obvious process people have been led to believe. I remember back in the spring of 1970, just after the New York abortion law had passed by a single vote in the legislature, I said to Dr. Abrams at the hospital, "You know, I'm scared to death of this new thing. I mean, what do I know about doing abortions? How many have you done?"

"About five, I guess," he replied. "The usual—therapeutic abortions for German measles, and for psychiatric reasons."

I nodded. Even before the new law, a woman could always get an abortion in New York City if she had enough money. All she needed was to have two reputable psychiatrists write letters saying that if she continued the pregnancy, she would commit suicide. Take those letters to a hospital, present them to the Abortion Board and they would allow her to be aborted. After all, if they had two letters, both claiming the patient was suicidal, what could they say? Prove it?

Dr. Abrams went on, "My wife said to me the other night, 'It's just like a D and C, isn't it?' So I told her, 'Hell, no.'"

"'Hell, no' is right," I replied. As interns we did D and C's, where we dilate the cervix and scrape the lining of the uterus. But a nonpregnant uterus is a rather firm organ. Put a curette inside and at least you can feel the uterine walls. A pregnant uterus on which you perform an abortion is soft. You can't feel the top of it. It's like curetting a cloud. You can perforate that uterus without ever knowing it and then have to go back and operate abdominally to repair the damage you might have done. So a lot of us were scared of the consequences of the abortion law. Doctors were saying they'd be damned if they were going to run around perforating uteri because the state legislature took a vote.

Well, we've gotten pretty good at this since the law went into effect. We're doing quadruple the number of abortions we did at first. Instead of scheduling one an hour and charging the patients accordingly, we're down to ten or fifteen minutes per abortion, and the cost to the patient has gone down correspondingly. But that scares me, too. The old adage about familiarity breeding contempt really applies: we can't afford to become too blasé about the whole procedure. If we ever lose respect for the machine we're working with, it will get us into one hell of a lot of trouble.

We don't use a manual curette anymore except in unusual cases. When the pregnancy is under twelve weeks, we use a suction curette, or vacuum aspiration. The little plastic pipe we put up into the uterus is attached to a vacuum, and we're sucking out the material under a considerable amount of pressure: 50 to 60 millimeters of mercury. We're scraping with the suction curette, too, moving it around to get the whole thing. After all, if there's a pregnancy on one side of the uterus and we don't move the curette around, we can miss the fetus. That's why people have been "aborted" and then six months later deliver a baby.

Now, as long as we stay inside the uterus, everything's okay. But if we put that suction apparatus outside—if we happen to perforate that soft uterus—then the machine can suck out lots of things, like a lady's intestines. The liberal press doesn't tell you about all the uteri that have holes in them and those that have been removed. So I don't think it ought to be said that abortions are the benign little procedures people would like them to be. Certainly this is no method of contraception.

Another reason I don't like abortions is that they're not very nice aesthetically. I don't understand how women can go to a clinic or hospital and have this done while they are awake. In some hospitals, only a local anesthesia is given. The area is blocked so there's no pain, but the patient is conscious. I wouldn't be able to stand it, to lie there and listen to this suction thing go *sworrpp* and then hear something splash into the bottle on top of the machine. It's bad enough for a doctor to hear, but how must a woman feel, knowing that splash was her fetus or baby that just got sucked out of her? Not only that, but in a lot of places the bottle sitting up there on the machine isn't changed between abortions. All the other apparatus is sterile and changed for each patient, but to save time, many clinics just let the bottle fill up. Can you imagine walking into a room where there was a bloody bottle full of other people's abortions? What I really dislike is the salting-out procedure. This is done when the uterus is too big or the pregnancy itself is over twelve weeks, so the abortion cannot be performed vaginally. In this instance, the doctor removes about 50 cc's of amniotic fluid by inserting a long hollow needle into the uterus and amniotic sac through the abdomen, at a point slightly below the navel. After tapping the amniotic fluid, he gradually injects 150–200 cc's of hypertonic saline solution into the uterus. The solution is lethal. It kills the baby in the womb. Then the woman whose fetus was too large to abort by suction curette must go through labor and finally, twenty-four or thirty-six hours later, exhausted, she delivers a dead baby.

Before twelve weeks, I'll abort someone if that's what she wants. Then the fetus is just an amorphous mass as far as I'm concerned. But when it gets to where I can recognize it as a human baby, or if it's twenty weeks old it may even have a fetal heart, then I won't perform an abortion except under unusual circumstances.

In my opinion, the main thing wrong with the present law is that it says you can be aborted anytime up to twenty-four weeks, meaning six months. I think the legislators were out of their minds when they passed this portion of the law. Most hospitals I know ignore the legal allowance and won't do abortions after twenty weeks. After all, at six months, you've got a living baby. If we took it out by Caesarean section, it's big enough so it might survive. Most babies don't survive until seven months, but it's possible at six. Now the saline we inject normally kills the baby, so it's born dead. But there's already been one case involving a woman who was carrying twins: when her doctor injected saline into one sac, one baby came out dead and the other baby came out alive. The doctor knew she had twins. Usually the substance from one amniotic sac passes into the other sac. But this time it didn't.

What must that woman have felt? The second baby finally died, but the question remains, what should a doctor do if it's alive? Are you asking him—or me—to drop it in the bucket? No. If a baby comes out of an abortion alive, I'll send it over to the premature nursery.

Another reason I avoid salting-out procedures is that I think they're terribly hard on the woman. Maybe this is just a rationalization. After all, if she wants to be aborted, I guess I should just accept her choice. But I'll let somebody else do it for her. After she's taken into a room where a doctor instills the saline into the uterus, she's sent back to her room and left alone to abort in bed. She's watched—there's always a nurse around—but she isn't in an operating room because you can't put somebody on an operating table and leave her there for twenty-four hours. There may be four women in the same room, all in various stages of labor or aborting. And of course they've all heard of the few babies that have been born alive so they're in constant fear that their baby is going to make a cry when it comes out. Then she finally delivers this thing, blood and all, right into the bed.

And so many times it happens at night. The woman must labor longer than a mother giving birth to a full-term baby because the cervix isn't ripe and nothing in her body is ready for the delivery. If we put the saline in at eight o'clock in the morning, it's three or four o'clock the next morning when she finally aborts. Then she's seen by the nurses on the floor but not by a doctor unless there's some problem. Hopefully the placenta comes out and this thing is whisked away. But sometimes she has to be taken to the operating room to get the placenta scraped out, then returned to bed to recuperate. I just wouldn't want a patient of mine to go through that.

When a woman comes to me for an abortion, I try to prepare her for what's ahead. First of all, I tell her not to look back. She's made her decision, and it's probably the only one, realistically, she can make. Even though it seems to be getting more popular for an unmarried girl to have her baby and keep it, most single girls really can't afford to raise a child. Actually, not many of the young single kids come to me. I suppose they go to clinics because it's cheaper and they don't want the family's gynecologist to know they're pregnant. Most of the women I see are married and feel they already have as many children as they want or can take care of. But single or married, too many crucify themselves with guilt after the abortion. I think it's time someone pointed out to them that this is a perfectly valid decision, and that they should either not feel guilty or realize that guilt is a normal emotion. Until recently, abortion was a dirty word. It referred to an illegal act done in the backs of candy stores. Suddenly it's legal and it's clean and it's to be socially and morally accepted. But a law can't change how people feel overnight. You can't spend most of your life being told something is bad and suddenly accept it.

Consider five patients going up to the operating room for a dilatation and curettage: we put them to sleep and do the procedure; then they go to the recovery room and everything's fine. But if we take five women upstairs to have abortions by suction curette, at least four of them will vomit as they're waking up in the recovery room. Now although an abortion is a more delicate procedure technically, it's practically the same operation as a D and C when you assess what has been done to the patient: same anesthesia, same operating room, same nurses, same doctors. Yet only an occasional D and C patient is nauseated whereas the vast majority of abortion patients will vomit. I think they throw up because of an underlying emotional feeling. Maybe they're trying to get rid of the baby or their guilt. Or maybe they're punishing themselves for having been "bad." Legal or not, an abortion is still a traumatic experience for most women.

There are exceptions, of course. I had an infertility patient, thirty-one years old, walk in pregnant one day. Married to a husband who had no sperm and who knew he was azospermic. It didn't take much to figure that one out. She was distraught as hell, obviously. Like a pregnant nun at that point. But she wasn't concerned over having an abortion. She was worried her husband would find out she had been pregnant and had gotten rid of the baby. She wanted the abortion and she didn't want him to know. In New York State, a woman can get aborted without her husband's consent, although she can't get her tubes tied without it. Anyway, we aborted her. It wasn't my position to ask questions. Some time ago this couple had put in for adoption, and after a long wait, had just gotten two little nonidentical twins.

Later, when this woman came back for her checkup, she told me the whole story. It turned out that the guy who had gotten her pregnant was a friend of her husband's. He also was married. The two couples used to go away on weekends together, and she said the other man kept "bothering" her all the time. After the abortion, she put a halt to their relationship because she wanted to keep her own marriage intact for three more months. At the end of that time, she and her husband could legally adopt the twins. Having accomplished this, she was going to reconsider resuming her affair or getting a divorce.

The patient seeking an abortion often wonders what I think of her, especially if she is unmarried. In the first place, I'm not here to judge. I'm only here to help. Besides, I would have no moral feeling against these individuals even if I were judging. I think that there but for the grace of God go most of us. These women unfortunately are pregnant because they did what everyone else is doing without getting caught. And I tell them it's normal to feel as though the whole world knows they're pregnant. They are not crazy because they imagine everybody they pass on the way to the hospital knows they're going for an abortion.

I also try to warn my abortion patients about what happens in the hospitals. First of all, there may be a lot of women arriving and getting "processed" at about the same time, 8 A.M. It's hard not to feel as though you're on a production line. Then, not every hospital or clinic works the same way ours does. We've turned over an entire hospital floor to abortions. There are no surgical cases. Certainly no babies—I mean, how cruel can you be? So every patient on the floor is in the same boat. And the staff has volunteered to be there, so there's no righteous finger-shaking. But I try to warn patients that there'll be all sorts of people on the floor: the seventeen-year-old single girl who tried it once and lost; the hardened girl from the East Sixties who was batting around and got caught; the married lady who has three kids and can't afford any more. There will be those women who don't want to talk, but there will also be some who will describe in detail exactly how they got pregnant, or by whom—sometimes with much glee. Actually, we doctors don't know all that goes on among these women before we finally see them in the operating room. I guess the lucky ones have somebody they can confide in so they don't have to go through this experience alone.

Physically there shouldn't be much pain after an abortion, although some women have cramps or abdominal discomfort for a little while. But there's more to abortion than the physical fact. I don't think people should be aborted and just turned loose. They should be able to sit down with someone and ventilate what they feel, or receive counseling. Unfortunately, this kind of help is too often unavailable. Also, some patients are actually discharged after an abortion without a word of advice about birth control. That just doesn't make sense. During the first year of New York's abortion law, something like six hundred women in New York City came back for *second* abortions. I guess it wouldn't be right to say that people should not be aborted unless they agreed to use some form of birth control in the future. But I do think there should be a lot of pressure and educational effort to get them to accept contraception.

I also think abortions have to be easily and perhaps freely available to poor people. Even $50 is too much for a poor person to pay. If she can go where people she knows have always gone—to the back of the drugstore for $15—that's what she's going to do. When they liberalized the law in California, there were just as many illegal abortions as ever because people still went to the old places for the smaller cost and fewer questions.

New York's abortion law is more liberal than California's, and we have a pretty good education program besides. I think there are indications already that fewer illegal abortions are being done. We're seeing fewer miscarriages, perhaps because a lot of the so-called "miscarriages" occurred when somebody was playing around trying to get rid of the child. Maybe an abortionist, or the woman herself, just stuck something up there and scraped a little until they started some bleeding; then the woman went home to miscarry by herself. We're also seeing fewer people with botched-up abortions. So I was distressed to hear all that foolishness from groups organized to fight for the repeal of this law, which I think has worked out pretty well. There have been few medical complications compared to the number of abortions performed. And as education continues, the proportion of early abortions is increasing, so the procedure becomes much safer.

Perhaps most important, abortion is getting to be less of a dirty word. Before the law went into effect, a lot of women would not tell us the truth about what had happened to them. We would say to them, "Now look, your life depends on whether you're telling the truth. Were you aborted, or was anything done?" They'd deny everything, and I saw women die under those circumstances.

I remember one married lady who had obviously been

pregnant until just before I saw her. The uterus was larger than it should have been, the cervix was open instead of closed and there was blood coming out of it. And she was sick. The question was, did she just have a spontaneous miscarriage or was something done that might have caused internal damage? We pleaded, *"Please* tell us, it makes a big difference if you had a miscarriage or if somebody did something. Maybe there's a hole out the back of your uterus." And she said, "Nothing was done. Absolutely nothing. I wasn't pregnant."

This woman went to her *death* denying that she had even been pregnant. We operated on her, but by the time she got to the hospital, she really was too far gone for us to expect much success. She had a badly perforated uterus, she was practically depleted of blood and she had an overwhelming infection in her abdomen.

I don't know whether she was pregnant by adultery and therefore would not admit it, or what. But the day after she died, her husband brought in a fetus he had found in the closet. It wasn't a big baby, and he had never known she was carrying it. When he brought it in to us he said, "I didn't know, I just didn't know."

Hopefully, this kind of tragedy won't happen anymore. In January, 1973, the United States Supreme Court ruled that abortions during the first three months of pregnancy are a private matter between a patient and her physician, and are not subject to state legislation. I heartily approve this decision.

16. A Dignity to Death

Eleanor Mays is a patient of mine who brought her mother-in-law from Dayton to see me. We operated on Mrs. Mays, Sr. in August and found that she had cancer of the cervix that had already spread to her liver. There was nothing we could do except to close her up and tell Eleanor that her mother-in-law didn't have long to live. She was seventy-four.

About six weeks later, Eleanor called my office: Mrs. Mays, Sr. had moved in with her son and daughter-in-law instead of going back to live alone in Dayton. Eleanor said the patient was getting worse and weaker and asked if I could come to see her. I told her that was impossible. We don't make house calls because it's difficult to do an adequate pelvic examination in somebody's bed.

Eleanor then brought her mother-in-law to my office, and it was obvious the woman was dying. She walked slowly, stooped over, supporting herself on her daughter-in-law's arm. We took her right away, of course. When I saw her, I didn't even do a pelvic exam because she was clearly debilitated and terminal.

You can tell most times when people are dying, not only of a cancer. The skin is pale. Not necessarily yellow, although people who have liver problems may have a yellowish tint. Otherwise the skin is a waxen white, and dry. When you pick it up, it has no elasticity; it's lifeless. And the eyes are usually sunken, with the cheekbones prominent.

If the cancer is at all advanced, we can recognize the disease. I've looked at a lady in the waiting room—a new patient —and said to my nurse or secretary, "Who's that? She's got a cancer." I went to a meeting recently and saw a doctor I hadn't seen for a long time. He was sitting up on the podium and I thought, "Uh-oh, I'm sure he's got it." We'll find out whether or not I was right, but he sure looked like it. We just have an intuition. Maybe it's the face. But a trained physician can tell. At the hospital I've said, "This woman smells like she has cancer." There's nothing scientific about a statement like that, but there is a certain smell to cancer victims. Don't ask me what it is because I can't tell you. And I'm not always right, but then we are not always right in anything.

Mrs. Mays's mother-in-law had lost a lot of weight and she looked like she came from a concentration camp. Her eyes were not clear, and she wasn't making sense all the time. She would drift off, and then come back. So we just took her blood pressure and pulse and helped her into a chair in my office. Then I took Eleanor into the examining room to talk.

"She's dying, isn't she?" Eleanor asked.

"Yes. I can't tell exactly when, but I don't think she has more than a few weeks left."

Then the question was, what should we do? The Mayses had three children. Eleanor was terribly concerned not just for this old woman but for her husband Jim, who had been watching his mother die, and for the kids.

"Jim says maybe we should put her in the hospital or a nursing home, but I don't think he really wants to," Eleanor told me. "He's just afraid of what it will mean to me and the kids to have her stay with us. I guess I'm afraid of that too. But how can we just send her off somewhere to die alone? I guess—" She hesitated. "I guess I need to know exactly what's going to happen."

"Does she still come to the table to eat?" I asked.

"She comes to the table, but she doesn't eat very much. We have to kind of force her."

"First of all, she's going to stop eating of her own accord, and you won't be able to make her eat. You shouldn't try. She'll take what she wants. After a while she'll stop drinking liquids. Then she won't come to the table anymore. She'll go to bed, and she has the type of disease—cervical cancer— where she will just go to sleep."

"What about the children?"

"As long as she comes to the table, there's not much you can do about it. Once she retires to her room, keep the children out of there. They don't have to watch her die. *Tell* them that Grandmother is dying. And tell them that they should stay out of her room."

Accepting all that I told her, Mrs. Mays decided to keep her mother-in-law at home, and I thought, "This is some fine lady I've got here."

Shortly after that visit, Eleanor called me in tears. Since she was in the neighborhood, I told her to come by. We were finished seeing patients but still working at the office. Eleanor's eyes were red and she started weeping again when she explained what had happened.

She had gone shopping in Bloomingdale's after work and had met one of her friends in the store. This friend was horrified at what Eleanor was doing. She told Eleanor her mother-in-law was going to start screaming in pain and the children would have to go through all that, and she said the old woman belonged in a hospital or home. Eleanor asked me if we would take her mother-in-law into the hospital.

"Sure, if you want to bring her in," I said. "What's she doing?"

"She's lying in her bed, and now she's sleeping most of the time. She hardly ever wakes up."

"Has she been screaming?"

"No."

"Well, she's not going to start," I said. "We'll take her in the hospital if you want. It's certainly a big job to have her at home. But no matter what your friend told you, she's not going to start screaming. Your mother-in-law has cancer of the cervix, and she's going to die of uremic poisoning once she stops putting out any urine. She won't know what's happening, and if there's such a thing as a pleasant way of dying, this is it."

"Oh, Dr. Sweeney, I know I shouldn't have listened to my friend," Eleanor wept. "But she just got me so upset." Then she said in a steadier voice, "I want to keep Grandmother at home—but I think she's in some pain."

"Well, give her the pills I prescribed. What do you care if you make her an addict? She's going to *die.*"

"But she won't take them."

"Okay, then don't give them to her. If she's in enough pain, she'll take them. And if she doesn't want to take them, don't force her. Why should we make her do anything she doesn't want to at this point? You're really helping her just by letting her die quietly, with dignity, surrounded by people who love her and whom she loves."

So Eleanor kept her mother-in-law at home.

On a fall day a week later, Mrs. Mays died.

I asked Eleanor if she and Jim and the children were all right, and she said, "Yes. I'm glad we kept her at home. I think we're all glad. I have to admit I'm relieved it's over, but it made us feel very close as a family."

So that's how it ended. This old woman got more love and better care from her daughter-in-law than she would have gotten in any hospital in the world. She didn't have tubes running out under each arm, urine coming from one tube and feces from the other. She just died peacefully in her sleep.

17. Beautiful Woman

Thanksgiving weekend: four days in the country. We drove north through a snowstorm, and I was glad to get out of the city, hoping we would have the first skiing of the year. This looked like a real vacation. I had delivered my next to last baby the week before and Marianne Dobbs wasn't due until January. With the weekend coming up, I could say it was nice not to wonder whose baby I was going to have to go back to deliver. But I missed it. Maybe not at 4 A.M., but all that happiness and excitement. It was hard to believe I'd gotten out of obstetrics. I sometimes wonder how I did it.

Of course I had to say yes to Marianne Dobbs: she lost three babies with me, and when she came in pregnant in May, I couldn't turn her over to anyone else. A lot of women who lose one or two babies will change obstetricians. Not Marianne. And she was due only a month over my final deadline. Anyway, I loved her.

Thanksgiving Day the whole family was over at our country place. I was watching football. The kids were all around, our parents, everyone. It was still snowing, and we were just about to sit down to Thanksgiving dinner at four-thirty in the afternoon when the phone rang.

"I don't believe it," I said, picking up the phone. It was Marianne.

"Dr. Sweeney, I'm bleeding and Dan's getting a taxi to take me to the hospital. I'm afraid there's quite a lot of blood."

"Do you have any pain or cramps, Marianne?"

"No, just blood. I've gone through two sanitary napkins, and I'm using a towel now."

"Any clots?"

"No."

"Are you lying down?"

"Yes. I was lying on the couch when the bleeding started."

"Okay, wait for Dan to come back upstairs and let him help you into the taxi. It's just a precaution, but I'm going to phone the hospital to have a wheelchair downstairs to meet you. It will take me about an hour and a half to get to the city, so there'll be another doctor there to take care of you. And Marianne, I know it's scary, the bleeding and everything. But you've had it before and it stopped. So try to take it easy, honey. We've gotten you and the baby this far and we're not going to quit now." Which was as much reassurance as I could give her, but not much at that.

I called the hospital to give Mrs. Ames some instructions and then I talked to Dr. Richards, the resident. "Try to get Dr. Abrams over there in a hurry. I think you're going to want some help. I've got a woman coming in with third trimester bleeding. She's not due for seven weeks. I can't tell if she's got a placenta previa or what. So be careful. She's had three miscarriages, and she has diabetes, so watch the infusion. I'm in the country and I can't get in for an hour and a half."

I hung up and jumped in the car and drove. We'd had

nearly three inches of snow upstate by then, and I'd been loving every flake because it meant skiing. But I was cursing it now. I was coming in so fast I hoped I would pick up a police car as an escort. None appeared.

Here was a woman—maybe the ugliest woman in the world on the outside—but she was beautiful inside. When she first visited me, Marianne was thirty-seven, tall, bony, dark-haired, as homely as Abraham Lincoln. She had been married for less than a year, and she came in right after New Year's, 1968, pregnant. She was a little old to be having a first baby. But everything was fine until she was ten weeks into her pregnancy. Then she had some slight bleeding. We told her to rest in bed, and the bleeding stopped. Again everything seemed normal until her sixteenth week of pregnancy, when her uterus stopped growing. We measure the uterus every time a patient comes in for her checkup. We waited two weeks and saw Marianne again and it still hadn't grown at all. Finally, we waited another two weeks, and by this time it was obvious that we had lost the baby. So in May we brought her into the hospital, induced labor and she delivered a deadborn infant.

We did a curettage afterward and everything went to the Path Lab. But the reports didn't show us anything to explain why her uterus had stopped growing.

Marianne got pregnant again at the end of 1968. In fact, it was in December because she told me this was the Christmas present she and Dan had given each other. Everything looked fine. But two months later she miscarried again. We brought her into the hospital to complete the miscarriage. The Path reports again showed us no reason for what had happened.

Marianne came to see me shortly after that and asked if I could tell her *anything,* because she and Dan still wanted to try to have a baby. That was in the spring of 1969. Marianne was thirty-eight years old and had lost two babies. What was I going to tell her? She wanted a kid more than anything in the world. I don't know if I would have had the guts to try again, but I told her I couldn't give her any medical reason why she couldn't have a baby.

And lo and behold, in August, Marianne missed a period and was pregnant. I told her all the things she shouldn't do: like have intercourse, take hot baths, fight the mob at Saks or lift anything heavier than was going to her mouth. And she should rest as much as she could.

Early in this pregnancy, she developed diabetes. That made it tough, because we had to control the disease and at the same time see that she didn't abort. But except for one minor episode of bleeding, Marianne was fine until her fourth month, when she started to flow. We brought her into the hospital so we could watch her closely and try to prevent a miscarriage. When the bleeding stopped, I said, "Okay, you have a choice: you can stay here or you can go home and stay in bed. You can't get up to do anything except go to the bathroom."

Now I was talking about five long months: it was November and she wasn't going to have her baby—if she got the baby—until the following April. But there was nothing in the world I could have told her that she wouldn't have done. She wanted this baby so much. So she went home to bed.

Then one evening she called me from home to say she was bleeding again. She was six months pregnant this time. She and Dan came into the hospital and within a couple of hours, she had cramps, went into strong labor and delivered a little boy. He only weighed a pound. Dan was there, holding her hand, murmuring endearments, and then the two of them began crying. They both saw their little boy delivered. He lived less than an hour, and I guess it broke their hearts. But it seemed to draw them closer together. I remember saying good-bye early that morning. I was feeling so depressed and these two people—Dan especially—tried to make *me* feel better.

The next few days while Marianne was recuperating, Dan practically lived at the hospital. He's a quiet, tall, balding man with a high forehead and a big crooked nose. He once had reddish hair and now has lots of freckles across his forehead. He made friends with everyone on the floor. We didn't put Marianne on one of the obstetrical floors—that would have been too cruel—so she was in a semiprivate room on the GYN floor. There were four in the room. One woman, an elderly patient, had few visitors and no flowers. Dan brought her a little bouquet the second day he was there. He helped the nurses with the trays, and you wouldn't have known he was in the middle of a personal tragedy. He would become quiet at times. But then he would talk to this old woman or someone else and he would come away feeling a little better himself. When I walked into the room on rounds to see Marianne, the three women who weren't my patients would tell me how wonderful this couple was.

I signed Marianne out of the hospital around the middle of February. The lab reports again came back negative. For the third time, we had no explanation for why this had happened. I saw Marianne in March, 1970, and again toward the fall, and she said she felt fine and things were going well between her and Dan. She had gotten her periods back, but didn't talk about having another baby.

And then came a day in the spring of 1971 when both Marianne and Dan showed up in my office. Marianne said they had tried to conceive, and although she had never had trouble before, now she couldn't become pregnant. The two of them sat there, two of the ugliest people in God's world, yet both so beautiful and so much in love. And they were both willing to do anything to get her pregnant.

What should I tell her? She was forty years old; he was forty-seven. Should I advise her not to get pregnant? The incidence of abnormalities in children of mothers over forty is huge. She had diabetes, and she had had three pregnancies with nothing to show for them.

So I told Marianne the whole story, including the fact that the chances of her having an abnormal child were 1 in 100. She said, "I just want a child. I'll take the chance. If it's got something wrong with its heart, I'll take care of it. Whatever it is, I'll take care of it."

This woman had all the reasons in the world to be bitter, but she wasn't. She wasn't angry at God or anybody else. She had accepted her ugliness, her diabetes, her loss of three pregnancies. And now she and Dan were sitting there having accepted their infertility, trying to find out what they could do about it.

I didn't advise her not to get pregnant. She was going to do it anyway if she could. On her chart I wrote, "Marianne and Dan are pretty old for this bit, but we should give them the benefit of the doubt and work them up."

We did a complete infertility workup on both of them and there was no reason why Marianne could not conceive. But she didn't. I talked to them about adopting a baby and taking some of the pressure off themselves. But they said they wanted to wait a while. They still enjoyed making love. It wasn't the mechanical thing it might well have become.

Then in April, 1972, more than two years after she lost her third baby, Marianne called up ecstatic: it was the twenty-fifth day of her cycle and her temperatures were up. She called back the next day and the next to tell me the temperatures were still up. Then one day there was a pinkish-brownish discharge. Marianne sounded whipped. Everything was lost. She'd done it again and now she was forty-one years old and had no children. Yet the temperatures were still up, and they continued that way, so in early May she came in, and Marianne was pregnant.

After that initial spotting, she didn't bleed during early pregnancy, and she was home, completely in bed. The only reason she ever left her room was to come to the office to be examined. We talked to each other every day on the phone, and everything seemed to be working out.

Then, during the twenty-eighth week of this pregnancy, Marianne suddenly became dizzy. She was nauseated and felt a ringing in her head. We were worried about her diabetes, a possible aneurysm (widening of an artery) or even the remote chance that she was developing a brain tumor. She was admitted to the hospital again, and seen not just by me but by other specialists. It turned out she had what's called Meniere's syndrome, which thank God is not a tumor and can be treated with medication. After two weeks in the hospital, we let her go home to bed. She was due the second week of January, and the question was whether she could keep this baby the full term of the pregnancy, or at least long enough so it would have a chance to live.

Marianne was one of the few patients who had my country number, and the last thing she said before I left was, "Have a happy Thanksgiving, Dr. Sweeney. I know you need a rest, so don't worry if I don't call you for a day or two. If everything's fine, I won't bother you at home."

And then I got her phone call: she was bleeding. Bright red. But no cramps. She didn't say she was terrified. It was obvious, though, that Marianne and Dan were scared to death they would lose this baby, too. So I drove like mad to get to the hospital, cursing the goddamned snow, although at least it seemed to be keeping some of the Thanksgiving traffic off the road. And I was wondering if this was a placenta previa, or a premature separation of the placenta.

The placenta supplies the fetus with oxygen and nutrients

mainly taken from the mother's blood. It also removes the child's waste product. When the placenta separates prematurely, before delivery, the oxygen to the baby's brain is diminished. If enough of the exchange surface detaches and it is too early in pregnancy for a Caesarean section, the baby is stillborn.

A placenta previa occurs when the placenta implants lower than normal in the uterine cavity, so that it is partially or sometimes totally covering the inside opening of the cervix. It's down there in front of the baby's head. A placenta in this position is more likely to tear and bleed, either before or with the onset of labor. Often there's a sudden hemorrhage with no cramps or pain, and a woman wakes up in the middle of the night to find herself lying in a pool of blood. This is her blood she's losing, and she can die unless she gets expert attention immediately.

Usually the bleeding from a placenta previa will stop unless there is some trauma, such as a pelvic examination, or unless the patient goes into labor. If we hospitalize the woman, keep her on strict bed rest and replace her blood loss by transfusions, it is possible to help her keep her baby until close to the end of her pregnancy. Then, if the placenta is located directly over the cervix, a Caesarean section is mandatory.

Finally, after what seemed like hours, I roared into the hospital and up to the delivery floor. Actually, it was just a little before 6 P.M. There were Dr. Abrams, Dr. Richards and Dan. Marianne was in a labor room, still bleeding but not heavily, and getting a transfusion. Dr. Abrams didn't know what was wrong because we couldn't examine her. It wouldn't help Marianne or the baby to have our fingers poking through the cervix and possibly into the placenta, where we might cause uncontrollable bleeding.

And I was thinking, "What do we do now?" I didn't want to perform a Caesarean if I didn't have to. Marianne had no labor cramps, and this baby was not due for another seven weeks. On the other hand, she was still bleeding. If it didn't stop, I'd have to get that baby out or lose it for sure. Fleetingly I thought of the fetal monitoring equipment on our obstetrical floor. Potentially a remarkable system that can give the obstetrician precise and vital information on the baby's condition inside the womb, it was useless now. We could not even examine Marianne vaginally, much less insert a cardiometer wire through her cervix and clip it to the baby's head to give a constant monitoring of the fetal heart. Nor could we insert the fluid-filled tube which would provide a reading of the pressure within the uterine cavity. All I knew was that so far, the baby was okay: we had a good fetal heartbeat.

Marianne and Dan didn't ask anything. They were faced with another disaster, scared but as brave as anyone I've ever seen, just hoping and hanging onto each other.

"The baby's fine," I said. "He's really pounding away in there." They looked at me, wanting to believe my words.

We have a gadget we can put on the woman's abdomen that magnifies the baby's heartbeat so everybody in the room can hear it. It's like a stethoscope but the sound goes into an amplifier before it comes out. We use this device, for example, if we're having difficulty hearing the baby's heart through the fetoscope. So I sent the nurse for a Doptone and put that on Marianne's abdomen. Suddenly it sounded like jungle drums.

"Oh my God, that's beautiful," Marianne whispered, and her eyes were glistening.

While the heartbeat resounded in the room, I went out to tell Mrs. Ames to prepare a team of surgical nurses and an anesthesiologist. During a holiday the hospital is down to minimal staff. If we had to do something in a hurry, I wanted some people standing by. Dr. Abrams offered to stay, but I thanked him and said I'd handle it, so he went home.

Then I returned to the labor room and we waited for another hour. It was close to 7 P.M. and Marianne was bleeding slightly. Every once in a while I'd put the Doptone on her abdomen and we'd all listen to the baby, its heartbeat steady at 140.

Suddenly Marianne gasped. Dan jumped a foot and I grabbed her wrist, pulled her hand off her stomach and put on my own. Her eyes were shut tight. Then they opened wide and she stared at me. "I think—" She stopped.

"I think you've just had a contraction," I said. "I think you're going into labor."

"Oh, Dr. Sweeney, I *can't,*" she pleaded. "It's much too early." The panic showed in her voice for the first time. Then she asked softly, "What's going to happen to our baby?"

I told her what I could. "Your baby's thirty-three weeks old, Marianne. He's a pretty well-developed infant at this point. With our modern pediatric care, he has a ninety to ninety-five percent chance of making it all right."

She reached for Dan's hand. "Of course." But I knew she didn't believe it.

We waited some more. In about twenty minutes, Marianne had a contraction that lasted for twenty seconds. I could feel it through the abdomen. Her uterus was hard. Marianne was definitely in labor.

She stopped bleeding during the next half hour, so I felt pretty sure she didn't have a placenta previa. The question was what should we do. Marianne was forty-one years old. Should we perform a Caesarean section or let her deliver from below? Women were meant to have babies following labor, and the baby does better when it comes through the normal birth passages because most of the mucus is squeezed out of its nose, throat and mouth during birth. With a Caesarean, the baby's in there one minute and it's out the next. So I preferred to deliver this baby vaginally rather than add the extra burden of a Caesarean section onto a premature infant. But it all depended on how the labor went.

Most of all, I wanted to examine Marianne, to rule out a previa and to evaluate the cervix. But suppose I was wrong. A vaginal examination could start a placenta previa hemorrhaging. We would have to be prepared for an immediate section.

I told Dr. Richards to get an OR team ready for a "double setup." Then we moved Marianne into the operating room, where I did a sterile vaginal examination with a full operating team scrubbed and ready to go if necessary.

But Marianne did not have a previa, and when I examined her, the cervix was already thin and 4 centimeters dilated. I ruptured the membranes in case we had been dealing with a partial separation of the placenta. This would reduce the pressure in the uterus and allow the blood to come out through the cervix instead of into the uterine wall. The amniotic fluid was clear, and I realized this might be one of the many cases where we would never know the cause of the bleeding.

We moved Marianne back to the labor room, but I told Mrs. Ames to keep the surgical team ready and to notify Pediatrics that we had a preemy baby and would want some help. Marianne was laboring quickly, like someone who has had previous babies. By ten o'clock, she was having good contractions every four minutes, and she was about 7 centimeters dilated. She was resting between contractions, but the pain was pretty bad when it hit. I didn't want to risk giving her any medication because of her medical history and because I didn't want to slow things down or take away any of her ability to push. My heart ached for her and I was hoping this wouldn't be a long labor.

By 11:15 P.M., her cervix was fully dilated but the baby's head had not descended deep into the pelvis, so I still had the option of doing a Caesarean. I told Mrs. Ames it was time for Pediatrics to send over the doctor. And I told Marianne she was fully dilated, because I wanted her to have whatever encouragement we could give her. She was exhausted from the pain and the work, and I wasn't sure how much more she could take. Dan looked as though he was being physically tortured. But Marianne started to push with her contractions, and the baby began moving through the pelvis. We wheeled her into the delivery room.

Then, around 11:50, the fetal heart fell precipitously to 96 beats per minute and all hell broke loose. I hit the emergency switch and Dr. Richards, Dr. Rogan, the pediatrician, two nurses, the anesthesiologist and an intern came running into the room. Marianne was gasping with pain. On the last contraction she gave a tired scream as she tried to bear down. If we put her to sleep now, we could well lose the baby. There were about eight of us rushing around the room, and Marianne was lying there watching and listening.

I told the nurses to put her legs in the stirrups. The anesthesiologist had already placed an oxygen mask over her face. We didn't have time to scrub so one of the nurses snapped gloves on both Dr. Richards and me. At the same time I called for forceps and a local for the episiotomy. Then, because everyone was getting too excited, I said very coldly, "Okay, now let's take it easy."

Marianne and Dan hadn't said a word.

"The fetal heart is still ninety-six," Dr. Richards told us.

The anesthesiologist announced Marianne's blood pressure reading and the nurse called out her pulse. Then I told Marianne that she still had some strength left and that the more she felt like she was being torn in half, the better the baby was coming. This great woman lay there hurting like hell, beat beyond belief, and then she pushed like nobody I've ever seen. Once she cried out, "Help me," but then she pushed that baby down until we could get hold of him for a good low-forceps delivery. I inserted the forceps and we cut the episiotomy and delivered a tiny premature male infant.

Dr. Rogan took him from me the minute I had cut the cord. I had sucked the mucus out of his nose and throat, and his skinny chest heaved once. As I handed him to Dr. Rogan, he let out a thin, mewing cry.

I swiveled back on my stool to be sure Marianne had heard the cry and was just about to say something when she started hemorrhaging. One minute everything was fine and the next, I had a pool of blood in the bucket at my feet.

"Get me blood and pump it in," I called out. The anesthesiologist switched the infusion while one of the nurses inflated the pressure cuff around Marianne's arm. Everyone except Marianne could see the blood pouring out of her vagina.

I think the most frightening thing in the world is a postpartum hemorrhage. But this was no time to panic. Marianne was bleeding so heavily she could lose 2,000 cc's or 4 pints of blood in a couple of minutes, and we couldn't replace it anywhere near as fast as it was pouring out. I had to discover where that bleeding was coming from and stop it before she went into shock or died. The most obvious cause was that the uterus was not contracting, so that was the first thing I went for. If the muscles of the uterus didn't clamp tight and close off the pencil-thick blood vessels to the placenta, nothing was going to stop the bleeding. I placed my hand on Marianne's abdomen but couldn't find the uterus. It was limp as a dishrag, a condition called atony.

I put my hand into the vagina and right up into the uterus —the cervix was widely dilated because the baby had just been through there. I felt the placenta, which had separated, and gently removed it. Then I put my right hand back inside and my left hand on top of her abdomen. I started massaging her uterus with my abdominal hand, trying to get the muscles to contract. The blood flowed down past my wrist.

"Put twenty units Pitocin in the infusion," I ordered.

"Dan," I heard Marianne say.

"Yes, sweetheart."

When I glanced up, the anesthesiologist was holding the oxygen mask over her face again. "Blood pressure's eighty over forty," he said.

"Her pulse is one twenty-six," a nurse said.

I kept massaging with my abdominal hand. And inside I did panic. It's an awful, sickening feeling. Doctors are no different from anybody else. If a patient is slipping away from us and going to die, we feel panicked. But we can't stop working.

I had about 1,500 cc's or 3 pints of blood at my feet when I felt the first reaction in Marianne's uterus. A little contraction or spasm. I kept massaging, and in another minute the uterus really started to respond. I was feeling stronger contractions. I kept massaging Marianne's abdomen until the uterine muscles were working again and I could feel the uterus under my abdominal hand. The bleeding had slowed. I withdrew my right hand and kept up the massage until finally the uterus was hard, or firm, like a large softball. Then the bleeding stopped. The blood was coming only from the episiotomy.

The fundus nurse took over the massage.

"Can you wipe me?" I was dripping with sweat.

I glanced at the anesthesiologist. The oxygen mask was off Marianne, and he nodded and said, "A little shocky but okay."

Dan was at the side of the table, rigid.

"She's okay, Dan. Just give her a few minutes."

I turned to Dr. Richards. "Give me a hand and let's examine the cervix and vagina before we do the episiotomy." I wanted to be sure Marianne hadn't been bleeding from a tear in the cervix.

"She looks awfully pale, Dr. Sweeney," was all Dan said while we worked. Then he suddenly got sick.

"Dan?" It was Marianne.

She was weak and bathed in perspiration, the sheets plastered against her.

"I'm here, love. I'm right here."

"The baby?"

Dr. Rogan was just coming over with their little boy all but hidden in swaddling clothes. He touched the baby to Marianne's breast and arm. "You have a boy," he said, "and I want to get him right down to the premature nursery."

"He's so tiny," she whispered.

Marianne and Dan stared. All they could see of their baby was his face, with bulging eyes. Marianne looked past Dan's shoulder at me. Her eyes widened at all the blood on my gown. Then she looked at Dr. Rogan.

"Please tell me if our baby's going to be all right."

"I think he'll be fine," Dr. Rogan replied. "We'll know a lot more later on."

Dan bent over the delivery table and wrapped his arms and upper body around the baby and Marianne, shielding them.

"I'd like to take him down now," Dr. Rogan said gently.

Dan straightened up, letting Dr. Rogan lift the infant. Then he bent down over Marianne again, holding her, kissing her, brushing back her wet hair. They were too overcome to say much. Marianne's eyes were closed and tears slid from the corners and ran down her temples into her hair. Dan kept embracing her while the delivery room emptied and the rest of us regained some composure. Then she opened her eyes and looked at Dan and me and said, "He has to live." And she fell asleep.

They took Marianne downstairs at 1 A.M. Dan and I went with her. He was gradually believing she was out of danger.

Then I took him to the preemy nursery, because he had hardly had a chance to see his son. I explained that Dr. Rogan had wanted to get their baby into a warm incubator as quickly as possible: after months in a hot uterus, any new-born infant is cold in the delivery room.

The pediatrics resident told us Dr. Rogan had been there until a few minutes before. Dan appeared shocked as he looked at his naked baby through the window of the nursery.

"He's so tiny," Dan said. "So thin."

You think of a baby as being chubby, but a preemy baby, thirty-three weeks old, has no fat pad beneath his skin. This baby's arms and legs were like sticks, sheathed in shriveled skin that closely outlined the bones except for a flabby fold around the elbows and above the knees. He looked like a skinny, withered old man, with a narrow neck and a few sparse hairs on his seemingly disproportionately large head. His tiny hands were not chubby at all. The skin there was translucent, pulled over the bones like the skin on an old person's hands.

Finally Dan asked me the question I'd been expecting. "Is he going to be all right, Dr. Sweeney?"

"It's too early to be sure, Dan. You can't just look at a preemy baby and prognosticate. He must be doing pretty well or Dr. Rogan wouldn't have left him. They'll know more tomorrow. The first twenty-four hours are the most important."

"He looks so fragile and helpless. There should be some way I could give him some strength—" Dan's voice broke and he stopped. "How much does he weigh?"

At birth he had weighed 2,200 grams, which is 4 pounds and 7 ounces, but I told Dan he would lose some weight at first. All babies do.

"When will they feed him?" Dan asked.

"They don't feed them for the first few hours," I said.

"After that, they'll probably put a tube down and feed him directly into his stomach. It takes a lot of strength to suck on a nipple, and he's so small he doesn't have the muscles—or he can't use them yet."

We went back to Marianne's room. Dan stood next to the bed in the dimmed light, staring down at her as she slept. . Suddenly he put his hands over his face and started to cry, sobbing silently, his shoulders shaking. I stayed with him for a while until he looked up, wet-faced, and said, "I guess that had to come out." Then I left.

It was almost 2 A.M. I told the floor nurse, "Call me if anything comes up. This is my last baby, and I'm sticking around." I called home. Then I went to sleep in one of the rooms they have for the attending physicians.

At seven the next morning I stopped by the preemy nursery before going to see Marianne. Dr. Rogan had already been back to see the baby, and the resident said he had seemed pleased. He had given it a 7 Apgar score in the delivery room, which is very high for a preemy. The Apgar is a simple test for evaluating a baby's condition at birth. The doctor scores five things—the baby's heart rate, respiratory effort, muscle tone, color and response to a catheter put in his nostril—and he gives a 0, 1 or 2 for each of these, making 10 a perfect score.

An X-ray of the baby's chest taken during the night showed clear lungs with no evidence of hyaline membrane disease, which used to kill many premature babies before modern intensive care nurseries were established. Chemical determinations on his blood reported a normal concentration of the electrolytes and oxygen and CO_2 levels. He was even considered strong enough to try bottle-feeding.

Breakfast was being served on the floor when I went to see Marianne. I had left orders not to wake her. She was asleep, and Dan was sleeping in a chair next to her bed. When I touched his shoulder he came awake with a start.

"Dr. Sweeney," he whispered. "Is something the matter?"

I motioned him to come out of the room.

"Everything's fine, Dan. I just saw your son. He's doing well. Did Marianne sleep through the night?"

"Yes, but she woke up once and made me promise to wake her if you came."

"Don't disturb her. She's exhausted. The best thing in the world for her is to sleep as long as she can."

"I promised," he said simply, and went back into the room.

Dan kissed Marianne and she came around more slowly than he had. But as soon as she saw me, she said, "Dr. Sweeney, did you see our baby?"

"I was just in the nursery and he seems to be doing fine," I said.

"Do you mean it?"

"I really mean it. How do you feel?"

"I wish I could see him or hold him," she said. "You don't know how much I just want to look at him."

"You'll be up before long and then you can go look at him," I told her. "He's in an incubator being fed so he'll be a big healthy kid who'll drive you crazy screaming and demanding attention."

"I'm going to love that," she said.

"How are you feeling?" I asked again.

"Can Dan see him soon?"

"Only if you answer my questions first."

She smiled. "I feel kind of tired but wonderful. I've never felt more wonderful. I've got absolutely everything now."

I leaned over and kissed her. "Congratulations," I said.

She smiled again.

I walked Dan back to the preemy nursery and introduced him to the doctor there. Then I said, "I think I forgot to congratulate you."

He looked at me hard. "And I think I forgot to thank you." He gave me a bear hug that nearly crushed my ribs.

I decided to skip breakfast and just go right home to my family. I got my car from the garage and headed onto the East River Drive. It was nearly empty. The sun was out and it was a gorgeous Friday.

PART TWO

Questions and Answers

A doctor spends a good deal of his life answering questions. Because of space limitations here, I have had to be somewhat arbitrary in selecting what subjects to discuss. Some of my comments in the following pages are simplifications of complex information. I don't think the lay reader will miss the technicalities I have left out, but in a sense, I miss them.

"This is not an obstetrical and gynecological encyclopedia, but a book meant to entertain and inform," I have been told by my coauthor and my editor. With this injunction in mind, I have tried mainly to answer some of the questions I am asked most frequently and to examine a few topics I think deserve more attention.

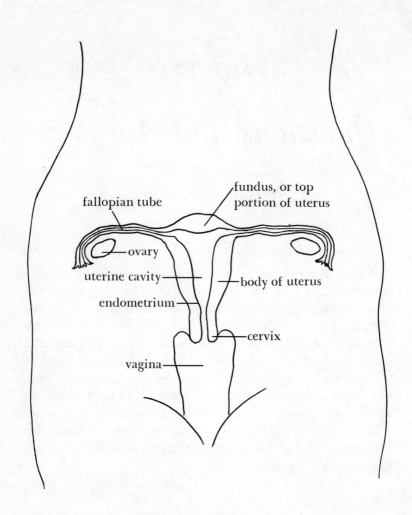

fallopian tube

fundus, or top portion of uterus

ovary

uterine cavity

body of uterus

endometrium

cervix

vagina

Internal female organs

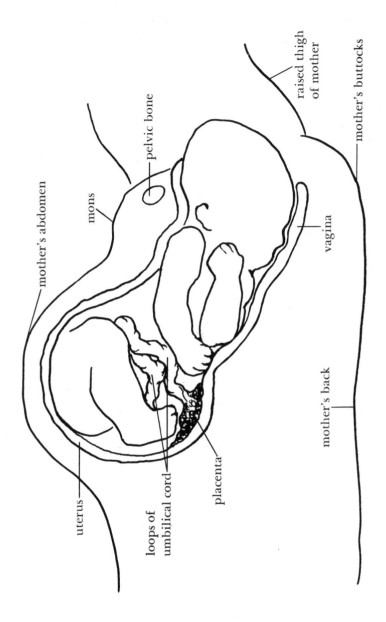

mother's abdomen

mons

pelvic bone

raised thigh
of mother

mother's buttocks

vagina

uterus

loops of
umbilical cord

placenta

mother's back

Childbirth: Baby's head is beginning to be born

18. Down There

I'm sure if I were a woman and reminded frequently of the complexity of my body, I'd ask my doctor a lot of questions about what was going on. Often a lady seeking information about some related topic suddenly admits:

You know, I don't really remember from school: how does the female reproductive cycle work?

Let's start right after a woman has her period. We'll assume she's in the reproductive age group and is ovulating. After each period is over, her cycle starts again, which means she failed to get pregnant last month and is preparing for possible conception this month.

Her two ovaries are full of thousands of eggs, or more precisely, follicles from which eggs can develop. Normally, except in the case of multiple pregnancy, one egg from one of the ovaries matures and ovulates each month. Surrounding this egg are cells which produce estrogens, or female hormones. During the two weeks the egg is maturing, these estrogens are excreted and put into the circulation. They work on the inside of the uterus, making the lining grow until it's thick enough to accept an egg that's been fertilized.

After about fourteen days, the mature egg breaks through the side of the ovary and is swept into the fallopian tube. The three days it then takes the egg to come down the tube is the time when fertilization can take place.

Meanwhile, the area of the ovary from which the egg came now produces progesterone, which stops the uterine lining from getting any thicker, and turns it into material full of glycogen and nutrients capable of sustaining the fertilized egg until it can make its own placenta. Actually, the ovary continues to make estrogens, too, but to a much smaller extent, and this fall in estrogen production may cause a woman to spot a little in the middle of her cycle. If the egg does get fertilized and implants, the estrogen-progesterone levels keep rising. If fertilization does not take place, these levels fall about two weeks after ovulation, and the woman gets her period on about the twenty-eighth day of her cycle. The lining of the uterus which is no longer needed is sloughed off.

Can a woman who has had one ovary removed have children?

Yes, assuming the remaining ovary, fallopian tube and the rest of her reproductive organs are physiologically sound. By the same token, a woman who has had an ectopic or tubal pregnancy requiring the removal of one fallopian tube can also become pregnant. A lady can even lose her right ovary and left tube and still conceive. The egg often "floats" across from the ovary to the opposite tube.

Why do I have menstrual cramps?

Because in effect, a woman is in miniature labor every month. When the endometrium, or lining of the uterus, is sloughed off during a period, it is expelled through the cervix by contractions of the uterus. These spasms, which start as a result of the fall in estrogen and progesterone, cause the cramps.

A woman whose cervix has been dilated by childbirth may have only mild cramps. A girl with a tight cervix may have more severe cramps. And someone on birth control pills probably will have no cramps, because most doctors believe the pills stop ovulation, and an anovulatory period is usually painless. The individual's pain threshold makes a difference, and psychological factors play an important role: if someone has heard since childhood that she'll have terrible pain when she gets "the curse," she'll sit there all tense waiting for the pain to hit—and it will.

How much blood am I losing? Enough to make me feel tired, or become anemic?

A woman usually loses only 50 to 70 cc's of blood each month—or between half a cup and a cup. If she is in good health she shouldn't feel this loss particularly. Unfortunately many women are chronically anemic, so even the loss of half a cup of blood may tire them. A good diet is obviously important, and bone marrow and liver are especially rich sources of iron, needed for the formation of new blood corpuscles.

Another thing that causes fatigue is the pain of menstruation. Pain is *tiring*. Everyone makes fun of cramps. I heard a comedian say that only married women have cramps. You go out with a single girl. She doesn't have cramps. Suddenly you marry her and she's having cramps. Well, there's nothing funny about cramps, and I don't think any woman should just suffer with them. She should take some analgesic, or pain killer. Or go to a doctor to find out why she is having cramps.

Can severe menstrual cramps mean something is medically wrong?

Yes. Although most cramps are from so-called normal causes, there are diseases that give you cramps. The most common of these is called endometriosis. This is a condition where some of the endometrium or uterine lining gets outside the uterus onto the so-called "implants" in the pelvis: the ovaries, tubes or ligaments. Then, the hormones that stimulate the endometrium *in* the uterus also work on the endometrium that is outside the uterus, causing microscopic bleeding into the implants. Having no way to slough off, the blood is trapped internally where it clots and scars the organs, causing pain or even sterility.

Some doctors believe endometriosis develops when part of the uterine lining goes back up the tubes instead of coming out through the cervix during menstruation. Other doctors think this is a congenital condition.

One way we can cure the problem is by removing the ovaries and uterus, thus stopping all bleeding. But this is too radical a step. There usually are ways of surgically destroying the areas of endometriosis so that the woman can still have children. Milder forms of endometriosis may respond to hormonal treatment. Finally, suspension of menstrual periods during pregnancy may cause a permanent remission of the endometriosis.

Other causes of painful periods include pelvic infections, a tipped uterus or fibroid tumors.

What are fibroid tumors?

They are benign or noncancerous growths which are relatively common in middle-aged women. Located in or attached to the uterus, fibroids are usually quite hard, composed mainly of fibrous and muscular tissue. They can be as small as a pea or as large as a grapefruit. Several small fibroid tumors may be present in one uterus without causing any symptoms. They do not become malignant and often no treatment is indicated, particularly with a small fibroid which is not increasing in size. A woman with a small fibroid in her uterus can generally become pregnant and deliver without complications.

A large fibroid tumor can distort the uterus and cause abnormal bleeding, pain or other complications, so that the physician may recommend surgery. Depending on many factors such as the size and location of the tumor, the age of the patient or her desire to have children in the future, removal of the tumor may or may not include a hysterectomy.

Why do I get headaches just before my period? Or pimples? Or have tender or swollen breasts? Or retain water and gain weight? Why don't I sleep as well? Why am I bitchy? Or tense? Or blue? WHY DO I FEEL SO DIFFERENT?

I'd hate to have to say which of the above symptoms are physiological and which are psychological, the distinction is such a fine one. But there's one thing we can be sure about. Did you ever hear the comment that "No girl can be a little bit pregnant"? Well, if you're talking about someone a week before the onset of her period, she is just a touch away from being pregnant as far as her hormone levels are concerned. They are at their highest point, and in many ways this lady is pseudopregnant: the egg isn't fertilized, but even if it were, her hormone levels would not be much different. They would only start changing after the egg implanted. So there she is, indistinguishable *in this regard* from the pregnant woman, and a lot of her symptoms are those of early pregnancy: headaches, complexion changes, tender or swollen breasts and water retention. All are typical.

Aspirin or some other analgesic may be adequate for relieving mild cramps and other physical discomforts. If she has a lot of water retention and swelling, there's no reason she shouldn't take a diuretic for a few days. Sensibly limiting her intake of liquid and salt before menstruation may also help.

I don't know whether anybody can really explain why women get blue or bitchy or tense just before they get their periods. Certainly you can't pooh-pooh these symptoms that are so widespread and say, "Ahh, there's another crazy woman with her psychological problems." Physiologically, her body chemistry is changing throughout the month.

Take being restless at night. Progesterone drives up your

temperature levels. If *I* took progesterone, my temperature would rise. So if your temperature is up and you sweat, you may not sleep well because you're hot or wet. Or the extra water in your tissues may be making you restless.

On the other hand, there's no question that a lot of the problems associated with premenstrual tension are psychological. If a woman is bitchy before she gets her period, she probably doesn't want to be pregnant, and until she bleeds, she's not sure she isn't. Or if she's expecting pain and doesn't like the messy business of having a period, why shouldn't she be upset? Who wants or needs it? Then, suppose she's more eager for sexual relations at this time: it may well be that subconsciously she feels the chances of getting pregnant are minimal, so she can relax and enjoy it.

Still, you can't dismiss these symptoms as purely psychological: what about a woman who has had a hysterectomy but whose ovaries have not been removed? Having lost her uterus, she's not afraid of being pregnant. She's not even going to get her period: she has nothing to bleed from. But because she still has her ovaries, she will go through the same premenstrual problems she had before. So we don't know all the answers to this.

Should I douche?

There are douchers and nondouchers. I'm an advocate of douching. I also brush my teeth every day. I think it's an old wives' tale that women should not douche—or should douche only once a month or once a week. The vagina is an orifice just like the mouth. There are cervical secretions in the vagina. If people are having intercourse, there are sperm in there, as well as bacteria, and this orifice can be washed out just like your mouth. So I think people should douche, two or three times a week. The vagina doesn't shrink or get dry, nor do any of the other things you hear about happen.

I'm sure that mothers in the past told girls not to douche

because that douche nozzle is a pretty penilelike object. They thought their daughters would become promiscuous if they started sticking this thing in the vagina. Maybe the girl would like it and start to masturbate a little, and of course there was the horror of catching your daughter masturbating with this nozzle.

What kind of douche should I use?

It wouldn't do any harm to douche with plain water, although since the vagina is mildly acid, most good douches are also somewhat acidic. I think one of the most old-fashioned douches is one of the best. It is also the cheapest. You put two tablespoons of plain white vinegar in a quart of warm water. Just be sure it's white vinegar: you're trying to clean your vagina, not pickle it! A great many commercial douches are really just white vinegar and water with a little perfume thrown in so they can charge you four times as much.

What do you think of the new feminine hygiene deodorants?

The main objection I have is that so many people are allergic to the stuff that's in them, and my patients come in here with all sorts of rashes and itches. You can get the same reaction from an antibacterial liquid cleanser or an antibacterial soap if you don't rinse it off thoroughly.

Obviously the vagina has an odor, but I see maybe fifty vaginas a day, and I think women have an exaggerated sense of that smell. In any case, I think a lady does much better to douche than to spray on Whatever-the-name deodorant. I suppose if you don't have time to douche, spray is okay as long as you're not allergic to it. But it's not going to do anything except put a little perfume down there, and maybe cut the bacteria level temporarily. Very temporarily.

Speaking of allergies and rashes, I don't usually get asked about cotton versus synthetic underpants until a patient already has a rash. As a doctor, I wish everyone wore cotton pants. Synthetics don't absorb any moisture. They keep that area nice and wet and macerated, and you can walk into my examining room and pick them right out—the women who wear cotton and the ones who don't. So as a gynecologist, I wish they'd never made synthetic panties. But as a man, I'm glad they did!

19. Birth Control

How does The Pill work?

The vast majority of doctors think the pill prevents ovulation, through a suppression of pituitary hormones. This would explain why women on the pill do not have menstrual cramps: anovulatory periods are painless. However, we are not certain why taking estrogen and progesterone, the ingredients in the pill, stops the ovary from ejecting an egg. A few doctors believe that ovulation actually does take place, but that the pill works on the cervical mucus, blocking sperm penetration and thus fertilization. Other doctors think the egg can be fertilized but the pill prevents it from implanting in the uterus so that it is simply "swept out to sea." Surprisingly, the exact working of the pill has never been conclusively proved.

Do you think the pill is safe?

Yes, or I wouldn't give it out. Originally, when only one company was in this business, there was only one pill: 25 milligrams of total steroids, which is a big dosage. I wouldn't give that to my patients. But we're down to half a milligram today, and I've come around to the position where I'm happy to prescribe it.

Now nothing in medicine is 100 percent safe and effective, and somebody's going to have trouble with the pill. But there are individuals who have trouble with aspirin. More people die from penicillin reactions than from birth control pills. Yet nobody to my knowledge has ever suggested that we take aspirin or penicillin off the market.

There is some evidence that the pill can cause blood clots since it makes a woman's body mimic pregnancy in many ways. Certainly there's a high incidence of blood clots in pregnant women. Nobody in his right mind is going to prescribe the pills to a lady with big varicose veins or a history of phlebitis. However, I think this symptom has been over-ascribed to the pill. I'm not entirely satisfied with how the statistics on the incidence of clotting have been gathered. And in any case, the risk is small—nothing compared to the risks of being pregnant. In the United States, the incidence of death from causes directly associated with pregnancy is 0.5 percent, or 5 in 1,000.

Can the pill cause cancer?

No. This is a completely unfounded fear that some people have. I'm a member of the tumor committee at the hospital, so this is something I'm constantly involved with. The only ingredients in birth control pills are estrogens and progesterone, either in combination or separately. A woman who is ovulating makes these hormones herself, each month. Since they are not carcinogenic in their natural form, what makes them carcinogenic when they are made up in pills? We use exactly the same agents to treat some cancer patients. It's been proven time and again that if we take a lady with a uterine cancer and give her high dosages of progesterone, the cancer appears to regress. We're not saying it's gone forever, but these hormones certainly are not carcinogens.

Then why do you have reservations about prescribing these hormones for some menopausal patients?

The menopausal patient has already had thirty to forty-five years of natural hormone production. When we prescribe hormones for her, we are artificially prolonging the stimulation of her tissues. Her tissues are no longer the same: they're older. I'm conservative enough to feel that we just don't know enough about cancer—what causes normal growth to change over into malignant growth—to prolong stimulation of the cells arbitrarily in cases where the woman has no menopausal discomfort. By the same reasoning, I don't see why someone who has had her ovaries removed surgically before she would have reached her natural menopause should not get replacement hormones.

Are there women you think should not be on the pill?

Yes. In addition to those with varicose veins or a history of phlebitis, I would not prescribe the pill to women with a history of hepatitis or impaired liver function, migraine headaches, leg or foot cramps, known or suspected carcinoma of the breast or any estrogen-dependent cancer or those with any undiagnosed abnormal bleeding.

Are there usually side effects from taking the pill?

Yes. Besides avoiding menstrual cramps, most women gain a little weight. The skinny might even consider this an advantage.

The second most common side effect we see with the lower dose pills is so-called "breakthrough bleeding." This is the bleeding or spotting which may occur while the patient is taking the pills. If it happens early in the cycle, I advise the lady to double up the pills for several days, and that usually solves the problem. If the bleeding is late in the cycle—that is, if almost all the pills have been taken—I advise discontinuation of the pills for that month. The patient then starts taking them again in five days.

The third side effect may be scanty periods. Some women would just as soon have no period, so this is really not too great a problem.

In the old days, a lot of people had rather unpleasant reactions to the pill: nausea, vomiting and headaches. Today these side effects rarely occur. We've come a long way since the time when we had just one pill to work with. Maybe that original lone product is why "the pill" is so often referred to in the singular. Today I must have a list of around twenty contraceptive pills. If one causes adverse reactions, I switch around until I find the right one. I think there's a pill to suit almost every woman.

Are there precautions women on the pill should take?

Yes. Besides notifying their doctor if they have any unusual symptoms, they should go back to him every six months for a complete physical examination including Pap smears.

What do you think of the diaphragm as a means of contraception?

I think it's fine, as long as the girl always has it with her and uses it properly. A carelessly inserted diaphragm may be worthless. One used after genital contact is much too late. A diaphragm should be inspected to make sure it's in good repair. It should also be used with a vaginal cream or jelly, for maximum protection.

Is the diaphragm as effective a birth control device as the pill?

Statistics on the comparative effectiveness of contraceptives vary enormously. The one fact most authorities agree on is that failures of the pill or diaphragm are usually owing to human error—the woman forgot her pill one day or didn't insert the diaphragm correctly. Generally, the pill when taken exactly according to directions is considered the most reliable —as close to 100 percent as any method we know. The diaphragm with vaginal cream or jelly also has a failure rate of less than 1 percent.

What do you think of intrauterine devices?

I don't like them because I don't think they work well enough. Some women's bodies simply reject them. Other ladies have adverse reactions, such as bleeding or cramps, and I end up taking out more IUD's than I put in. Finally, even if the IUD stays in and does not cause any bad reactions, in my opinion it is not as effective a contraceptive device as the pill or the diaphragm. We have all delivered women with IUD's in their uteri. I even did a Caesarean section on one woman where I took out the device first and the baby second.

What do you think about vaginal foams, or creams and jellies?

If used consistently and properly, the foams provide a fairly good vaginal barrier; I would rate them midway between the diaphragm and a group of jellies and creams for use alone.

What about vaginal suppositories or tablets?

They are about as effective as creams and jellies alone. Statistics on their failure rates vary considerably, starting at about 2 percent and going up. This is not a widely used method in the United States, although it is popular in Japan, particularly among the low socioeconomic groups.

What about the rhythm method?

This involves a high pregnancy risk. The rhythm method is based on abstinence from intercourse during the woman's supposedly "fertile period" of the month. The problem is that as of this writing, there is no practical way to accurately pinpoint the moment of ovulation. It is here that this method of "Vatican roulette" fails.

What about simply douching?

High pregnancy risk.

What is coitus interruptus?

Coitus interruptus, also known as withdrawal, is intercourse with the man withdrawing his penis from the woman's vagina before ejaculation. It is the oldest method of birth control still known to be practiced, and it may be the most widely used method in the world. I agree with Dr. Mary Calderone, who states, "Coitus interruptus is a method that is always available and that costs nothing. It should be learned for those situations in which no other method is at hand."

What do you think of condoms?

The condom is probably the most widely used mechanical method of contraception in the world. Its main drawback is the complaint from both sexual partners of the loss of full sexual sensation or satisfaction. Nevertheless, if used consistently and properly, condoms are effective.

Will there ever be a perfect contraceptive?

I don't know if we'll ever have a perfect one, but something better than the devices we now have will come along. There is already a pill that makes men temporarily infertile. But it will never sell because you get sick if you drink any alcohol while you're taking it. Researchers are working on a pill that will make women infertile for as long as a month. And scientists are having some success with a "morning after" pill—a contraceptive you take after intercourse.

What is a female tubal ligation?

This is a procedure in which the fallopian tubes are severed or tied off, making it impossible for the egg and sperm to meet. Since the procedure is usually permanent, it is a form of sterilization rather than contraception.

Can a woman get her tubes tied on request?

In New York State she can. Laws vary from state to state, just as abortion laws differ. Many hospitals handle tubal ligations through a meeting of a special board of doctors. These are usually all men, and they decide whether or not a woman will be allowed to have her tubes tied. I think that's wrong. I think, regardless of how many children a woman has had, or whether she's married or single, if she says, "I want to have my tubes tied and I'm aware that it's a permanent thing," then she should be permitted to have the operation. Fortu-

nately there is a trend today toward liberalizing the circumstances under which tubal ligations are allowed.
How are tubal ligations performed?
There are several ways. We can get to the tubes through the abdomen, which makes it abdominal surgery, or through the vagina, which makes the operation less major. With both of those procedures, what we generally do is pull the middle of the tube up into a loop, tie and cut the loop part off. In time as the suture is absorbed, the two ends of the tube fall apart so there is a space between them where the loop portion was removed. The egg then can't make a continuous passage down the tube.

There is a new way to do tubal ligations using an instrument called a laparoscope. This is the so-called "Band-Aid sterilization." We make a tiny incision about an eighth of an inch long right in the navel, so when it heals, there is no visible scar. Then we fill the abdomen with carbon dioxide, inflating it like a balloon. Next we insert the laparoscope, which is a long tube that transmits light through thin transparent fibers. Through a slight magnification in the eyepiece, we can actually see the ovaries, uterus and tubes. We make a second tiny incision in the lower abdomen, put another instrument in and hold onto the tubes, cauterize them and cut them. Those patients are home the same day. (Some doctors use only one operating laparoscope and work directly through it, but I personally prefer the second instrument.)

Under what circumstances is a tubal ligation not a permanent sterilization?
In one procedure, the end of the tube is simply buried between two layers of the peritoneum or lining of the abdomen. Theoretically, we could reestablish continuity between the ovary and the tube by freeing the buried end. But that technique isn't used very much because usually we're doing tubal ligations for a patient who doesn't want any more children.

What most people are not told is that a certain percentage of tubal ligations will fail, and women who have been told they have been permanently sterilized will come back pregnant. Failure rates vary from less than 1 percent to over 7 percent, depending on the particular group of women being followed up. I doubt that many ligations performed by skilled gynecologists fail, but it's certainly possible for the tubes to recanalize if the procedure is not done correctly.

What is a vasectomy?

The male equivalent of a tubal ligation. The vas deferens, or duct that transports the sperm from the testis to the penis, is tied off. This procedure is 99 percent effective, and relatively simple. It can be done in the doctor's office under local anesthetic. Usually a urologist performs this operation. However, if the urologists in a community are not in favor of vasligations, or vasectomies, this is the one operation that the American College of Obstetricians and Gynecologists will allow us to do on males.

What do you think of vasectomies?

I think they are a highly legitimate means of sterilization. I don't think a vasectomy demasculinizes a man, although psychologically most men in this country haven't accepted them. There are many urologists—males—who won't perform the operation on other males. Yet most gynecologists—males—will tie a lady's tubes. That's not fair. If a couple has decided they don't want any more children, and if we can do a minor procedure on the male, without the dangers inherent any time a patient undergoes general anesthesia, then I think the minor procedure is the logical, legitimate one. Actually, we are already getting an increasing number of inquiries about vasectomies, and as time passes, I'm sure they will become more and more popular.

20. Modern Times

What do you think of sex today?

I love it!

Does it worry you that chastity or virginity are becoming less valued by young people?

No. I don't mean I'm in favor of promiscuity, but as a gynecologist and therefore a part-time de facto psychiatrist, I think one of the worst things that can happen to couples is to begin marriage as virgins. I know it's going to be difficult for me to talk to my daughter this way. I'll do it, though, because I believe she'll avoid a lot of marital problems.

Nowadays, I suppose there are not many virginal brides around. But those who are virgins face a real emotional trauma. You can't take twenty years of teaching and just throw it out the window. All those years, Mother told you sex was dirty, and if anyone looked at you there or touched you there, my God, you should run and tell her. Then suddenly they say you're man and wife and you're supposed to dash into the bridal room, throw off all your clothes, hop into bed and say, "Take me, I'm yours," and everything should be fine. But it's not.

When you get right down to it, what's the big deal about virginity? Why is it all right for a boy to be running around sowing his wild oats when the same behavior is frowned on for a girl? And what *is* a virgin? Somebody who's never had intercourse? Suppose a couple has participated in every other sexual activity: petted, kissed each other on the lips, kissed each other genitally—everything except putting the penis in the vagina. Is the girl any more a virgin because she hasn't done that one thing? I've seen "virgins" who were pregnant because the guy ejaculated, without actual intercourse, in a position where his semen could run into her vagina.

There are so many old wives' tales connected with "losing your virginity." People think there's a hymen that has to pop or bleed. But there's no membrane across the opening of the vagina with the Good Housekeeping Seal of Approval on it. Really, the hymen is just a little double band of skin *surrounding* the opening to the vagina. Girls can put Tampax in their vaginas before they've ever had intercourse without breaking this little ring, because the hole is there and it's not covered. And little girls put lots of things in there: fingers, paper clips, pieces of cotton, and they're still virgins.

If the hymen is torn at intercourse, what happens is the little ring of tissue tears a bit because it's too tight. But it also stretches, and some married women come to my office with the hymenal ring still intact. We do exams on little girls— insert a speculum in the vagina and look at the cervix—and they don't go away "deflowered." Now in olden times when they married off little twelve-year-old girls to mature men, sure they bled. Today, however, you don't have to tear or bleed the first time you have intercourse. It doesn't have to hurt, either, especially if the girl has been using Tampax, or if she's been riding horseback or doing any of the other athletic things girls enjoy.

Do you think people are going too far in the sexual techniques they practice?

No. I think the kids today have a better attitude toward sex than we had. If two people both enjoy what they're doing, I don't see anything wrong with any heterosexual or, as a matter of fact, homosexual act. I don't think the homosexual should be laughed at or ostracized, although I don't want my daughter or son to become one. And if anal intercourse is fun for two people of the same or different sexes, I don't see anything wrong with it.

I certainly don't believe what I was taught as a medical student: various forms of stimulation were all right as long as they led to "normal sexual activities." We used to hear the word *perversion* whenever anything other than penile-vaginal intercourse was discussed. Oral-genital manipulation was always discussed in terms of a perverted act, although we were told, "It's all right if it ends up with normal intercourse." Well, if somebody enjoys cunnilingus, what's wrong with it? That's the point, isn't it: for both people to have fun?

What do you think of smoking marijuana to heighten sexual pleasure?

I don't know what sex is like with grass. The kids say it's best that way.

A model came to see me—a tall, good-looking single girl, twenty-six years old, wanting to know if she was built right. She said she'd been having intercourse since she was eighteen and she had an excellent sex life with no hangups. It didn't make any difference to her what she did or how she did it. She enjoyed every minute. Then one day she smoked some grass before making love and she said, "Wow. I never had an orgasm like that before in my life. I did it again and had a great orgasm again. Now I think I'm so hung up about orgasms—I've only had really great ones when I've been on grass—that I can't have any without it. That's crazy. I can't always smoke grass first. So I want to know if I have all the necessary equipment. If everything is physically okay, I guess I'm going to go to a psychiatrist."

What was I going to tell her? Go home and smoke grass? I told her she was fine physically and I didn't have an answer to her problem, but maybe the psychiatrist would. I don't know whether she had better orgasms with grass or whether they just seemed better. With some people, I'd figure, okay, the inhibitions are gone when they're on grass and therefore they can lie back and enjoy it. But this was not an up-tight girl. She said she'd had no inhibitions about sex in the past and had always enjoyed it, and I believed her.

Why is VD such a problem today?

Largely because there's a lot more intercourse going on. Add the fact that some of the VD organisms are becoming resistant to the drugs we're using in treatment, and it's understandable that we're back on a venereal binge.

How many people does it affect?

In the United States, from July, 1970, through June, 1971, there were 624,371 *new* cases of gonorrhea reported by U.S. public health officials, plus 23,336 new cases of syphilis. But these figures barely hint at the actual number of people affected because they only represent new cases. Also, the disease often goes undiagnosed. Finally, although this is required by law, a large majority of diagnosed cases aren't reported to the health authorities. According to the American Social Health Association, a private organization that studies these diseases, gonorrhea is the most prevalent communicable disease right after the common cold. It ranks No. 1 among reportable diseases, followed by scarlet fever and streptococcal sore throat, mumps, rubella, hepatitis, tuberculosis, measles and so forth in descending order.

Is VD more prevalent among the lower socioeconomic groups?

Absolutely not. This is one of the basic misconceptions people have. VD is the ultimately democratic disease.

Are syphilis and gonorrhea the only venereal diseases?
No, there are several others. But the ones we're seeing commonly are syphilis and, more especially, gonorrhea, also known as "the clap."

Can syphilis or gonorrhea be caught by kissing?
Yes, if the person has an infection where you are kissing him or her.

Can they be caught from toilet seats?
In most cases, no. The organisms which cause the diseases die quickly when exposed to air. However, recent investigations have shown that sometimes the organisms survive long enough for the infection to be acquired from contact with inanimate objects previously used by an infected person.

What causes syphilis?
A microorganism called a spirochete (*Treponema pallidum*).

How does syphilis develop?
Acute active syphilis occurs between ten and forty days after the spirochetes enter the body. The first sign is usually a sore or chancre (pronounced "shanker") which appears at the point the organism entered the body. The chancre may look like a pimple or blister or punched-out ulcer. The spirochetes that cause the disease can be recovered from this lesion. It is highly infectious. If a man has a chancre on his penis and a woman has genital relations with him, she may get a chancre of the vulva or, more frequently, of the vagina. If she has oral-genital relations with him, she can get a chancre in her mouth. However, men or women can get chancres of the rectum, or even on the hand or elsewhere on the body, especially if there is already an abrasion in the skin.

The chancre presents a big diagnostic problem because it's painless and it may be so small or hidden that it isn't noticed. This is particularly true if the chancre is inside a girl's vagina. In addition, blood tests are negative more than 70 percent of the time during this early stage, although if the primary lesion can be found, it can be scraped, sent to the lab and the organism identified. Eventually the chancre will go away on its own even if it's not treated, so people think they're scot free at that point; but the infection doesn't go away. They still have syphilis and will show other signs as the second stage develops.

What are the signs of the second stage?

Usually a mild skin rash anywhere on the body appears three to six weeks after the first sore. Other symptoms may include sores on the mucous membranes inside the mouth or sexual organs, fever, headache, sore throat, falling hair, eye inflammation, swollen glands or any combination of these. During the second stage of syphilis, the infected person is also very contagious. A blood test at this point is conclusive, but the symptoms may be mild enough so that they are never brought to the doctor. Or they may be misdiagnosed. Several of these symptoms in combination may sound like a cold or flu. To make diagnosis more difficult, these signs too will go away on their own without treatment.

What happens next?

Probably a third of the victims of syphilis will undergo a spontaneous cure. Another third will retain a latent form of the disease. Years later, the final third will suffer destructive lesions of the nervous system or heart, resulting in possible blindness, insanity, heart disease, paralysis, painful deformity and occasionally death. In 1967, the last year for which data are available, there were 2,400 known deaths from syphilis in the United States.

What is the treatment for syphilis?

Long-acting penicillin is effective against the syphilis treponema in all stages of the disease.

What is gonorrhea?

A bacterial disease caused by the gonococcus organism, *Neisseria gonorrhoeae.* Gonorrhea is highly contagious and may cause pain and sterility, but it is not a killer in the way that syphilis is.

How do you get it?

The same way you get syphilis. Gonorrhea can be transmitted through the mucous membranes of the genitourinary tract and also through the rectum or the mouth or even something as simple as a cut on the finger. If you have the germs on your hands and happen to rub your eyes, you can get a bad eye infection. Gonorrhea is a systemic disease. That is, it isn't limited to the genital tract. Gonorrhea arthritis is caused by the same gonococcus organism we're talking about.

How does gonorrhea develop?

The onset of the disease usually occurs between three and ten days after exposure. In men, it typically consists of a penile discharge as well as pain on urination owing to inflammation and swelling of the urethra. This is something a man will notice, so he'll generally go to a doctor for treatment. One of the insidious things about gonorrhea in women is that a lady can have it for a long time without any symptoms or with such a fleeting symptom that she disregards it. There are no sores or chancres from gonorrhea, and every woman has some sort of discharge, so she may not think it's symptomatic of anything. Other possible signs in women include burning on urination, soreness and swelling of the vaginal opening, abdominal discomfort and chills or fever. Again, these manifestations can be absent or so mild that the woman with gonorrhea may well be old Typhoid Mary spreading the disease without knowing she has it.

Another disturbing thing about gonorrhea is that there's no foolproof diagnostic test. We take cultures and about 40 percent of the time, we can't find anything. That doesn't mean the woman doesn't have gonorrhea. It just means that in seventy-two hours, the lab couldn't grow the gonorrhea organism out of her culture. So we treat her anyway. She has to get 4.8 million units of penicillin in any event because I wouldn't take the risk of not treating her. If gonorrhea is allowed to continue untreated, the infection can result in severe, painful pelvic inflammatory disease and may cause sterility because of damage to the fallopian tubes. It can injure a man's sperm ducts, causing pain and sterility.

If the symptoms of gonorrhea are so mild at first, how does a woman know she has it?

Usually because a boyfriend has called her and said *he* has gonorrhea. A man doesn't ordinarily have a discharge, so if he suddenly develops one, he knows there's something wrong. What's appalling to me is that in this day and age, the guy's doctor sometimes doesn't take a culture. I've had more than one girl come in and say her boyfriend had developed a discharge and had been given penicillin by his doctor.

"Did his doctor take a culture?" I'll inquire.

"I don't know."

"Call up and ask."

She'll call her boyfriend and he won't know.

"Have him call the doctor and ask," I'll say.

So she'll do that and then report that her boyfriend's doctor hadn't taken a culture. "It looked like gonorrhea," the doctor said. Looked like gonorrhea! What kind of answer is that? It's a lot of trouble to take a culture, there's no question about it. We hate them, because it means my secretary has to leave the office and take the culture tube immediately to the hospital. But cultures have to be done. Otherwise, the girl whose boyfriend was treated without a culture has to take the penicillin shots as a precaution even though he may not have had the disease.

What is the best protection against VD?

1. Abstinence.

2. The condom—assuming the penis or vagina are the infected areas, and assuming the condom is used during the

entire period of contact. But you can get pregnant in spite of condoms, because they have holes or aren't used soon enough or fall off, and you can get a venereal disease in spite of them. If both partners wash the genital area with soap and water before and after intercourse, this will also reduce somewhat the chance of infection.

I suppose eventually we'll discover a safe, effective drug and, hopefully, an immunizing vaccine. Meanwhile, we've got to rely on better education and we've got a real and growing problem on our hands.

21. Obstetrics

Because of the enormity of this subject and the number of detailed books for laymen, I'm going to limit myself mainly to personal observations and areas where I disagree with or question prevailing obstetrical practices.

What is an obstetrician's biggest complaint?

Fatigue. When a mother comes back for her six-weeks visit and I ask, "Is the baby sleeping through the night?" and she says, "No, not yet," I say, "Now you know what an obstetrician feels like all his life: chronically tired!"

Do you have any complaints about patients?

I can't stand women who are unhappy because they got a girl and wanted a boy or vice versa. I had one patient who had three girls. She wanted a boy in the worst way and there was no question in her mind, that's what this baby was going to be. When she came to the office, she always talked in terms of "He . . . he . . . he." There was complete silence in the delivery room when I told her the baby was a girl. No happiness, nothing. I deal with too many people who wouldn't care what they had—they'd take a hermaphrodite if they could just have a kid—to stomach this. And here was this bitch lying there with a beautiful little blonde girl she wouldn't even look at.

However, most women are great. They don't care what they have as long as it's healthy. If it is a girl and the mother thinks her husband wanted a boy, that's her second fear: that he'll be disappointed. Maybe he is, a little. I think most husbands probably want a boy first. There's this male ego that you've got to perpetuate the name and all that crap. Usually, though, the husband takes one look at his baby and he loves it, whatever it is. Or if he's still a little sorry he didn't have a son, just wait a few months until the baby girl reaches up to be held in Daddy's arms: he melts, and that's the end of his disappointment right there.

Isn't it unfair to make allowances for a man who wants a son and yet expect a woman to be above preferences?

It certainly is! But that's how most mothers are.

Can you tell me what kind of anesthesia I will have?

Almost all expectant mothers ask this question. Yet the information given to them is often as inadequate as the anesthetics still being used in many delivery rooms in this country. One problem the doctor faces in discussing anesthesia with a patient is that he can't commit himself about what he will do until he sees how the labor and birth are proceeding. At that time, he will constantly weigh three factors: the comfort of the mother, the welfare of the baby and the progress of the labor itself. However, he can tell his patient in advance what the most likely alternatives will be.

What is the difference between an analgesic and an anesthetic?

Analgesics, which include aspirin, Demerol and morphine, dull or diminish pain by raising the patient's pain threshold. Local anesthetics blot out all sensation by blocking the sensory nerves that communicate with the brain. A general anesthetic eliminates pain by rendering the patient unconscious.

For many years we gave laboring mothers morphine. It not only dulled the pain but induced a sense of euphoria. The use of morphine was stopped because it was thought to be too strong a depressant on the baby. It's important to remember that most drugs given to the mother pass via her bloodstream through the placenta to the fetus. However, recent tests show that morphine may have been wrongly condemned, and the use of this analgesic is being reevaluated.

Meanwhile, Demerol is the drug most commonly used to reduce labor pains. There is a limit, however, to the amount of Demerol we want to give since it also inhibits the baby's respiratory center. Fortunately, drugs are available that counteract the effects of both morphine and Demerol if they do cross the placental barrier.

What is Scopolamine?

An amnesic drug that does not diminish the sense of pain but erases the memory of it afterward. A lot of doctors combine it with Demerol. If it's used properly, I don't object to it. But wiping out the memory of pain is certainly no substitute for the relief of serious suffering. If Scopolamine is not used correctly, it makes a patient act almost crazy. Under its effects, women may throw off their covering and come out with four-letter words that you can't believe they know, much less would utter. Besides, it can make a patient physically violent. I actually saw a lady break her nose on the end of the bed under the influence of Scopolamine. Yet there are hospitals not far from New York City where patients with football helmets on them are put in padded beds, "scoped to the eyeballs," and they don't even know what's happened when they wake up hours after the birth of their baby.

Is there a safe anesthetic for a woman who still has several hours of labor left?

Yes, there are three in particular which I think should be much more widely employed. These are the paracervical, the epidural and the caudal block. Each involves conduction anesthesia, which means anesthesia that acts locally, or regionally. Because it does not enter the mother's bloodstream, as does a general anesthetic, it cannot cross the placenta and affect the baby.

The paracervical block is injected in two places, on either side of the cervix. It deadens all the pain of the expanding cervix and actually aids in dilatation. Since this anesthesia does not affect the abdominal or uterine muscles, it doesn't take away the patient's ability to push or bear down. But as it does not block the vagina and perineum, an additional form of pain relief is required for the delivery.

For a while paracervical blocks were the fad, but they have become less popular. Probably one reason is that this is not the easiest injection in the world to give. The doctor has to make sure he's not putting the needle in the baby's head, which is right there above the cervix. And he has to avoid getting into a blood vessel that would carry the anesthetic quickly into the baby, possibly causing some transient changes in the infant's brain waves. Some doctors never got the necessary experience and don't want to take a chance doing this procedure. I think it's up to them to get the experience.

Another reason paracervical blocks are not used more is that they might have to be given every forty-five minutes or every hour during labor. They take time to do and more time while you wait around to be sure everything's all right. With so many busy practices, obstetricians unfortunately don't have all these hours to spend with the patient. Or they don't want to be up all night giving anesthesia. But I don't understand why the young doctors on the house staff don't do more paracervical blocks. The man on the delivery floor at night is up —or he should be. He's not being paid to sleep.

The epidural block in my opinion is the answer to most women's prayers. I think it should be the universal obstetrical anesthetic used. The epidural, administered in the back at waist height, can be given in any stage of labor. Since the thin tube originally threaded through the needle is left painlessly in place, the anesthetic can be renewed as needed, without additional injections such as the paracervical requires. Depending on the amount of anesthetic given, most or all sense of feeling in the uterus, vagina and perineum is eliminated. In contrast with the paracervical block, no further drug is needed even when we're ready to cut the episiotomy.

Because the needle does not enter the spinal canal, the epidural eliminates the dangers of a spinal anesthetic. "Epi" means outside; "dura" is the covering that separates the spinal canal. Thus with an epidural, there is no chance of an infection, like a meningitis, inside the spinal canal; nor is there the possibility of damage to the spinal cord itself.

Then why isn't the epidural the perfect anesthetic and used all the time?

First, it's technically difficult to give properly, so some doctors avoid it. Second, in most hospitals, the epidural must be administered by an anesthesiologist, and it may have to be renewed every hour. Third, if too large a dosage is given, the patient doesn't feel anything; her muscle power is gone so she can't push. Therefore an epidural can slow down labor. However, if the anesthesiologist is good, he can control his injections so that the patient is still aware of her contractions although she has little real pain. Properly given, an epidural can speed labor. Finally, many doctors have the misconception that an epidural automatically requires a forceps delivery and they avoid it for this reason. It does increase the likelihood of forceps, but with the muscles so relaxed, this delivery is a very simple little operation, no harder on the baby than a spontaneous delivery.

What is a caudal?

A caudal is very similar to an epidural, except that it's given down by the tail-bone in what is called the caudal space. It, too, can be administered at any stage of labor and can be renewed periodically through a thin tube left in place. Because the caudal blocks the nerves so low, a forceps delivery is the rule.

What about gas?

I object strongly to inhalation gas as an obstetrical anesthesia. Usually it's nitrous oxide and oxygen. It is a general anesthesia that rapidly crosses the placenta and produces very sleepy, inactive babies. I suppose in cases where there is no time to administer another kind of block or where a woman doesn't want to be awake when she's delivering, an argument can be made for the use of inhalation anesthesia. But nowadays, at least in good obstetrical hospitals, I think it's being used less and less, and conduction or regional anesthesia is being substituted.

What is a pudendal block?

The pudendal block is an anesthetic for delivery, administered in the delivery room. It deadens the perineum and whole vaginal area, as opposed to a local Novocaine injection, which just blocks the perineum where I'm going to cut the episiotomy. A pudendal eliminates the pain caused when the baby's head comes through the vagina, and assuming I have time to do it, I think it is more effective than the local infiltration. It involves two injections on either side of the vaginal opening, with the needle leading in toward the area where the pudendal nerves are located.

How is labor induced?

We can give women oxytocin or Pitocin to put them into labor. Buccal oxytocin—"buccal" means mouth—is like little chiclets which we place on the gums above the teeth, to be absorbed gradually. We can also give the drug intravenously, in which case it acts faster.

What do you think of inducing people?

I don't think there's anything wrong with it. There are those who call this meddlesome obstetrics, but I believe inductions are perfectly justifiable even for nonmedical reasons.

Any doctor who tells you he only induces patients on a medical basis is lying, because he does it sometimes for his convenience and sometimes for the woman he's delivering. I had a lady who lived out on Long Island. She was terrified of that Long Island Expressway on a summer night. When she got to term, we induced her rather than have her risk getting stuck in traffic.

As long as inductions are managed properly, they're just like normal labor. I mean the object is not to shoot the kid across the room and catch him in a basket. One precaution I do think should always be taken is to give the patient a trial of induction before the membranes are ruptured. Then you can quit if you've "picked it green" as we say—that is, if the cervix isn't quite as ripe as you thought it was and the woman doesn't go into labor the way you expected. If you've already rushed up and ruptured the membranes, you're committed; you must deliver. You can give her drugs to try to ripen the cervix, but you may end up doing a Caesarean section.

Why does a woman delivering her baby routinely have an episiotomy?

The standard answer to this is that without an episiotomy, the pressure of childbirth will probably cause the perineum, or skin between the vaginal outlet and anus, to tear. If we make a nice straight incision, it's going to be easier to sew up and it will heal better than a ragged tear. Under the circumstances, I agree with this procedure—but I'm not sure the position we use for hospital deliveries in America is really the best one. It's called a dorsal lithotomy position: the woman lies on her back with her feet up in stirrups and her thighs and legs spread wide apart by knee rests. That puts a big strain on the perineum, and I think when we stretch the skin there so tight, we increase the chance of its tearing when the baby is born. If a lady precipitates or gives birth to a baby in bed, everything's relaxed and usually she doesn't tear, or at least not as badly as when she's up in stirrups. Most primitive people deliver in a squatting position or use an obstetrical chair, thus taking advantage of the force of gravity. Or they lie on their side. A woman in labor turns on her side if you leave her alone because the pain is less severe. In England, patients are delivered that way, and it's called the Sims position. But it doesn't fit in with U.S. hospital routine. Of course it's easier to work on a patient when her legs are up.

But isn't the episiotomy a relatively minor detail?

Not to the patient, although she may feel embarrassed complaining about it. I'm always amazed to see the blasé attitudes that people have toward episiotomies. Even the nurses are the same way. But put the same length incision on a man's abdomen and it's a major abdominal procedure. He's not turned loose from the hospital to go home in four or five days —much less to go to work taking care of a child. He's sent home in ten days.

I sometimes wonder whether mothers really get enough rest in the time they spend in the hospital. Granted there are places in the world where you go into labor, squat, have your baby, put it on your back and then go on picking rice. But that's not necessarily good. When my patients ask me how soon they can go home after delivery, I tell them they can stay as long as they want for themselves, but they've got to stay five days for me. After all, an episiotomy is two inches long on the outside but it's another two inches long on the inside—it goes up into the vagina, and muscles and all sorts of things are cut. And not only is it a four-inch incision, which is bad enough, but you've got to *sit* on it. That's awful when you think about it. No wonder we see new mothers walking around the halls dragging their legs. It hurts!

22. Surgery

Is surgery very difficult?

The decisions that may have to be made in the operating room are sometimes the most difficult in the world. However, surgery itself isn't very hard. All you do is clamp, cut and tie. There are many myths about how delicate surgery is— like the one that you have to have small hands to be a good surgeon. That's a myth perpetuated by surgeons with small hands. I could take my fourteen-year-old in there and scrub him and say, "Here, pick up the knife, cut here, do this, do that . . ." and he could probably get through an operation that wouldn't hurt the patient. After I've stood there operating for eight hours, removed a woman's uterus, bladder and rectum and brought the colostomy with the feces out one side, and another loop of bowel with the urine out the other, of course I'm exhausted physically and emotionally. But it's a lot less difficult to know *how* to perform an operation than it is to know *when* to. We spend a lot of time teaching that kind of judgment to the interns and residents.

Are most surgeons more skilled than other doctors?

276

No. There are some surgeons who are never going to be any good. They are all quick to count how many operations they've done. However, you can do a thousand operations in the wrong way, or a thousand you didn't have to do—the number doesn't mean anything. We had a beautiful surgeon at the hospital. His hands were gorgeous. He could do everything. Technically I think he was the best I've ever seen. But I always thought about this man that there was a block somewhere between his head and hands: his indications for operations often didn't seem right to me. If my wife had needed to be operated on, I'd have loved this man to do it—as long as another doctor saw her first, made the diagnosis and then told this surgeon exactly what to do. I admired his skill but I didn't trust his judgment.

There are other surgeons who I don't think are particularly skilled. Not all doctors are good doctors; not all surgeons are good surgeons. It's frightening to think that the man with the knife may be mediocre, but not all professional ballplayers are Willie Mays, so why would you expect all surgeons to be stars?

Is a certain kind of man more apt to become a surgeon?

Yes. You know, "When in doubt, cut it out," is a surgical dictum. We're aggressive. Obviously, it's the disease, not the patient, that we're attacking. And if we get a cancer case, that's when the aggression really comes out. When I have to teach the residents I say, "If you're not going to be aggressive with this disease, you're never going to be a cancer surgeon. Go do something else." And we can spot them pretty early—the young medical students or interns who will be happier just doing obstetrics or maybe, later on, obstetrics and gynecology, but not cancer surgery.

Are gynecological surgeons different from general surgeons?

Yes. First of all, we spend more time trying to save an organ than trying to remove it. It's one hell of a lot easier to take something out. With an ovary, for example, two clamps, snip, gone, and five minutes have taken care of the ovary. But to remove the cyst and retain the remaining part of the ovary and make it functional takes a lot longer. Also, general surgery doesn't usually carry with it the same intimate, emotional impact. Don't misunderstand—it's important surgery. It may involve somebody's gallbladder or stomach or appendix or even somebody's heart. But in our field, if a woman wants babies, whether she's going to have them or not depends on what we do. And there's a lot more emotion attached to an operation on someone's reproductive or sexual organs than to most other operations. Finally, the gynecological surgeon is more likely to be involved with his patient: often he's known her for years.

What do you think of the doctor shows and surgery on TV?

I enjoy them. They must have doctors advising the writers or directors, because most of the programs are pretty factual. Of course, they're unrealistic inasmuch as no doctor could do all the different things some of these TV guys do. And there are minor discrepancies. For example, in a TV operation, there's always an electrocardiogram hooked up, with a little bleep showing the heart beating. That's very dramatic, and I suppose every operating room in the world ought to have one going, but many don't. The machines are expensive. And if you have an anesthesiologist sitting there who's on the ball, it shouldn't be necessary. Also, on TV, if the patient isn't breathing for himself, there's always a respirator breathing for him. That's the accordionlike machine you see going up and down. But a lot of anesthesiologists prefer to pump the bag by hand. Automatic respirators aren't used in real life to the extent they are on TV. On the whole, though, I think the shows give a lot of useful information in an entertaining format.

Do you have any comments about treatment of postoperative patients?

There are two areas where I disagree with commonly accepted practices. First of all, I think the catheter, or tube inserted into the bladder to empty it, is one of the most lethal instruments in the hospital. There are more infections and problems caused by inserting a tube through that dirty urethra from below than you would believe. Consequently very few of my patients get catheterized. You don't have to put a catheter in. She'll void. I always hear things like, "When she did void, she must have had seven hundred cc's of urine in her bladder." So she had 700 cc's or a pint and a half of urine. I'm sure that if the person who said that had been out drinking beer one night, he had 700 cc's of urine in his bladder. Yet he wasn't being catheterized because of it.

Most people don't know they "can't" void after an operation. *I* tell them they won't have any trouble voiding. So that's a little bit of hypnosis or suggestion, if you will, that has already been laid in before they go to sleep. And the great majority of them have no trouble. I think most catheters are put in patients because the nurses don't want to take the time with the bedpans. It's so easy to slip in the catheter, hang a plastic bag on the side of the bed, and go off.

Now people who have had bladder operations are different. You have to drain those bladders somehow. But I usually stick a needle in through the abdominal wall and drain the bladder through what's called a needle cystotomy. They don't get infected if you put a sterile needle directly into the bladder. I don't catheterize even for the radical procedures. If the bladder gets too full during the operation, I'll stick a needle into it and drain it off.

I also disagree with the practice of leaving dressings on for several days. If the incision is well approximated and everything is fine, I take the dressing off after twenty-four hours and leave it off. I think the patient heals better that way.

23. Cancer

People are more frightened of cancer than of any other disease. Heart disease is much more lethal, but it doesn't sound as bad. We were raised that way.

Most people don't ask questions about cancer until they or someone close to them gets it. Then, to the layman, all cancers are one disease and the minute you say the word, the death knell has been rung. In fact, there are many different kinds of cancers, some more malignant than others, and a person who has a cancer is not necessarily going to die from it.

What's going to happen to me?

This is the first question people ask. Many times the doctor can only describe the treatment, not what the outcome will be. There's a certain host relationship which people have to their cancers. In other words, some people can contain their cancers better than others. We can't explain why. I remember one cancer patient who was sent to a terminal-care home. Five or six years later, she got tired of "terminal care" and left. So even when you have what appear to be advanced lesions, they won't necessarily kill you. The host relationship always has to be taken into account.

Doctors always talk in terms of "five-year survival." It's been found from experience that if a patient goes five years without persistence or recurrence of her disease, then her chances of living for a long span are good.

In what areas do women most frequently get cancers?

In the breasts, cervix, uterus and ovaries.

Why are regular gynecological examinations so important?

Cancers don't start overnight. It's not normal tissue one day and cancer the next. There's a gradual change from normality to malignancy, so if women will come in to be examined, we can pick up that change.

I think Pap smears have done more than anything else to increase the detection of early cancers and decrease the incidence of advanced cancers. And I think it's an affront and a shame that George Papanicolau didn't get a Nobel Prize in medicine. The man's dead now, but he probably saved more lives with his little Pap smear than anybody in the history of medicine ever saved with a shiny knife. I never heard him complain about it, but I think he deserved that recognition. He was a sweet old Greek man, a dear, dear person. He and Mrs. Pap used to do the smears, and they trained hundreds of people in his laboratory. Now, of course, Pap smears are accepted worldwide.

What does a Pap smear show?

The Pap smear was never meant to be the basis for a diagnosis. It's just a warning that something is wrong in the cervix or vagina. When I take a Pap smear, I do three things: I reach into the vagina and remove a little bit of the vaginal discharge, or pool. Then I go into the cervix and scrape a bit of the inside and put that on some slides. And I also take some of the outer cervical wall. These are just exfoliated cells —cells that have been shed and will be examined by the lab. It's as if some bricks fell off a building and you picked them up on the street and noticed they were defective. A Pap smear can tell us we've got some defective bricks or cells, and we'd better go back where they came from and make a histological diagnosis by taking a little piece of tissue.

What are the signs of cancer of the uterus?

Abnormal bleeding is the only symptom. However, bleeding can be the result of many causes other than cancer—such as hormonal imbalance.

Since uterine or endometrial cancer is primarily a disease of older women, the bleeding is usually postmenopausal. A D and C is mandatory in all cases of postmenopausal bleeding, and it will give a conclusive diagnosis. Pap smears are of little or no value in detecting cancer of the uterus because the endometrial cells normally do not exfoliate. Furthermore, uterine cancer is often accompanied by a stricture of the cervix, so the cells cannot get down into the vagina.

What are the signs of breast cancer?

The early sign is a painless lump. More advanced symptoms are a retraction or dimpling of the skin over the lump, and a painless lump in the armpit.

I think women ought to examine their breasts themselves, every day. You've got to take a shower or bath every day, so you can certainly feel your breasts. You won't know what you're feeling, but if there's a change, you can go to your gynecologist immediately. Why are people dying of breast cancer, anyway, when there they are, right out in front of you?

What are the symptoms of cancer of the ovaries?

Ascites, which means the abdominal cavity is full of fluid, is the only noticeable sign. Unfortunately, by the time this symptom appears, the cancer is usually too advanced for us to save the lady's life. Ovarian cancer is a highly malignant disease.

Am I going to have surgery?

There are three accepted ways of treating cancer: surgery, irradiation and chemotherapy. Treatment varies according to the natural history of the particular variety of cancer. People have the idea that cancer is like a fungus creeping all over everything. Maybe this awful sense of a disease spreading everywhere inside you is one reason the very word is so frightening. But it isn't that way. There is a definite pattern to how and where each type of cancer spreads. One cancer may be an inch separated from another, yet the two go entirely different ways. Cancer of the cervix spreads laterally, shutting off the ureters, while cancer of the endometrium, or lining of the uterus, never does.

Most laymen quite naturally think the thing to do is cut everything out as long as the lady is operable. And there are certain cancers where radical surgery is the treatment of choice, such as cancer of the vulva or breast. These patients do poorly with radiation. Yet with cancer of the cervix, X-ray gives the best results. It often kills the cancer and stops it from spreading.

Do nonmedical considerations influence decisions about cancer treatment?

For me they do. I think cancer raises a tremendous philosophical as well as medical question. There is a certain dignity to death that I believe we as physicians should never forget. We should permit people to die decently.

I always remember a patient who had cancer of the cervix —the mother of a nurse in our hospital. She was seventy-one years old, and she had already lost one kidney from the disease. We treated her with X-ray therapy, because she had an advanced lesion to start with. The cancer didn't stop. It was growing toward the side of the abdomen with the good kidney.

Now the question was, should we go in and do a colostomy? Bring the bowel out to the skin on one side, and put the ureter, or tube that leads to the kidney, into another loop of bowel and bring that out to the other side. Or should we leave her alone? She wasn't in agony. Did we have the right to take this woman, aged seventy-one, and risk the one kidney she had left? She wasn't in the best medical condition to start with. And if we performed the surgery, what were we giving her even if we were "successful"?

Well, the daughter insisted her mother be operated on, so we went ahead and did the colostomy. Now this woman had feces coming out into a bag on one side of her abdomen and urine coming into a bag on the other side. Then her cancer started to grow.

We had deprived this woman of her natural death. Her cancer would have obstructed the ureter of that remaining kidney, and she would have died a quiet, painless uremic death. We prevented that. When the cancer started to grow, there was no way for this poor woman to die. Her cancer ate a big hole into her lower pelvis. It spread into the bones in that area, and she was in agony. Sometimes there's just not enough morphine to stop the pain, and it's illegal to administer a dose we know is lethal. So here was this woman, suffering excruciatingly, filthy and smelly. You couldn't stand being in the same room with her. The family couldn't bear it. She couldn't stand herself. She used to *beg* us to kill her. Her cancer was actually growing out of her pelvis. She couldn't even sit because of the pain from it: she was sitting on her own cancer. I can't ever forget this woman lying there screaming in pain and begging to die. So there's a lot to be said for sometimes doing nothing.

Aren't you playing God when you make that kind of decision?

Maybe. But in my decision to operate on somebody, I'm playing God to a certain extent, so why can't I make the decision *not* to operate? Why am I playing God more if I make the one decision than if I make the other?

Then what guidelines do you go by?

I don't think people should be hurt. If they're going to be hurt by your treatment, don't treat them. That's one reason radiation therapy may be the treatment of choice, instead of surgery: radiation may obtain a remission or cure of the cancer. At least you're not going to give the patient a hideous living death. To me, any time the treatment is worse than the disease, something's wrong.

I remember a patient who was presented as a case at another hospital. This was an *eighty-four-year-old blind lady* on whom they'd done a total exenteration: they took out her bladder, her rectum and her uterus. Then they brought the colostomy out one side and the urine out the other. This blind lady lived alone. It was the most sickening thing I ever saw in my life. How could she ever take care of herself? Why had they done this to her? Just to prove that they could treat her lousy disease? That some guy was the biggest surgeon in the world? What was the point of subjecting this old woman to the dangers of an operation, not to mention the fact that she was better off with her cancer than with what they did to her? I got up and walked out of their conference. I just couldn't face this woman.

Why don't you ask the patient what she wants?

That's not our job. Our job is to make a decision, based on everyone's experience and ability, as to what would be best for a particular patient. This question comes up a lot at the hospital, and I always tell the medical students, "You must go to the patient with a recommendation, not with, 'You can have this done or that done, you decide which you want.' She can refuse, but she's not qualified to make a medical decision that you can't make."

She may ask, "What's the alternative if I don't follow your recommendation?" Then you give her a straight answer. Sometimes it's that nothing else can be done. And she may say, "Screw it, Jack, you're not going to do that to me." That's her prerogative, too. It's her body.

Do many people refuse to have radical operations?

Some do. I don't know of any statistics on this. You'd have

to define what *radical* means. I can sit here and say, "I wouldn't want to go through life without a lower jaw. I wouldn't think it was living to stay in a room with two or three holes in my neck, my lower jaw having been removed, afraid to go out, not wanting my children or grandchildren to see me." But I don't think anyone can tell how he's going to react as a cancer patient until it's his turn. When you are face to face with death, you may hold life so precious that you'll grab at the chance of prolonging it under any conditions. So I'm just talking through my hat when I say I wouldn't submit to a horrible operation—maybe I would. But I doubt it. Patients who have these radical procedures often say they're sorry afterward. But until you undergo the experience, it's hard to really believe there are things worse in life than death.

Do you ever allow a comatose or terminally ill patient to die?

Yes.

How is such a decision made?

We discuss the situation with the family and follow their wishes. Sometimes the relatives start out wanting us to do everything possible for their loved one. Then, after keeping a vigil with a living corpse, they may change their minds. Plenty of people, after they *see* what's happening, say, "Okay, now let's stop this. Let's leave Mother alone and let her die." And then we can stop the support. We can pull out the tubes. Again, I don't think we're playing God. We're not going to kill this woman, but we can avoid using all the artificial gadgets just to keep her heart going. If it were up to me whether or not to maintain this kind of terminal support, I would always decide not to. I don't see any reason to maintain a life that's not living. That's the dignity in death I was talking about.

Of course, if a family wants us to maintain support, we do.

And there are some relatives who will cling to a corpse as long as the beloved person is alive in any sense of the word. But I think you have to define what living is. The dying woman who lies there whimpering, maybe waking up occasionally or maybe completely comatose: is she alive because her heart is beating? I remember one husband whose wife went into a coma. He left the hospital and never came back to see her. He said that as far as he was concerned, she died that day. And when she finally died, it was the daughter who came in and took over. I couldn't decide how I felt about that husband. I disliked him at first for leaving, yet I understood his point of view. He deeply loved his wife, and he was not a cruel man to start with. If he had been, I'd have hated the son-of-a-bitch. But he loved her and was attentive to her while she was ill as long as she was conscious. What bothered me most was his letting his daughter take over the final arrangements. That was a little tough.

This question of "When is a person dead?" is becoming more and more important in hospitals. A heart transplant is going to work a lot better if the transplanted heart is still beating. Now, they hook up an electroencephalogram to the donor's brain and as soon as it goes flat, when there are no more brain waves, they pronounce that patient dead. His heart may still be beating, or fluttering, but the donor is legally dead.

Should a patient be told if she has cancer?

I think people should be told where they stand. I try to treat my patients the way I would like to be treated. If I get cancer, I want to know. There are some things I might want to do in light of that knowledge. I tell my patients, *"I will not lie to you.* You don't have to wonder, 'Is he telling me the truth? Is he telling my husband or daughter something that he's not telling me?' " Then I warn them, "If you don't want to know, you'd better go somewhere else. Don't play games with me. I won't play games with you." And I haven't had anyone get up and leave because of that statement. Sometimes the families are shocked, but not the patients.

I don't mean you have to come out bluntly and say, "Well, Mrs. Jones, you have cancer." She can be told in as gentle or hopeful a way as possible. She can be told that she has a serious problem, at which point she'll probably ask, "Do I have cancer?" If I'm lucky I can say, "Yes, but it's treatable and possibly curable, and this is what we're going to do to help you."

They know, anyway. At least among the somewhat educated population, it's rare for a lady to receive X-ray therapy or radium treatments and not know she has cancer.

I've seen families destroyed by hiding knowledge from the patient. I'm thinking of one family in particular. The husband had been a high-ranking naval officer who died just after the Korean War. The son was an Annapolis graduate, and the daughter a lovely, black-haired black-eyed girl engaged to be married. The mother had untreatable cancer, and the family said, "Don't tell her. It will kill her." Well, the daughter made up some reason for putting off her wedding. She and her brother went to sit with their mother—there was someone in there all the time. But nobody talked. Silence, practically. They were so afraid that one of them would say something that wouldn't jibe with what the other had said. And they had to check with each other to get their stories straight. And my God, the mother suspected, but she was afraid to talk to them. They were all she had, but they were all playing games. Where was the love and support this woman needed?

Finally I said, "Look, this is ridiculous. I mean, there's your *mother* in there. Tell her you love her or something."

They were afraid they would break down. So I said, "I'm going to tell her."

I went in and said, "Mrs. O'Neil, I want to tell you something. I'm terribly sorry, but I think you should know. You do have a cancer." And I had to say, "And you're not going to get better."

"Oh my God, the poor children. Do the children know?" Not a word about herself. Her first thought was the children.

"Yes, the children know."

And it was beautiful to watch this family come together again. Now they could talk. She was a brave woman. Most people are, especially women. That's the way they're made. Their thoughts are for the people around them. Now this family was talking away. Mrs. O'Neil had things she wanted to do, belongings she wanted to give people. All sorts of things could be taken care of. Friends could be talked to. The feeling wasn't, "This is the end of everything for everybody," but, "Now I know what I want to do."

Certainly there's going to be some lady who's told she has cancer who will jump out the window. People have gone out of windows at my hospital. It's sort of a favorite hospital for that, it's so tall. And there are people who have gone home and jumped in front of trains. But I've also seen people go out of windows who didn't have cancer but thought they did. And they jumped because they believed they weren't being told the truth.

Do you think that cancer should be a medical specialty in itself, like pediatrics or gynecology?

I have mixed feelings about this, although I would tend to say no. There is a growing drive today to create specialty boards—oncology boards—for doctors who just care for cancer patients. I can understand that this may be a good idea, because if a physician deals only with cancer every single day, he may be better at it. Perhaps people with cancer should be transferred to hospitals where just that disease is treated. But suppose you live in a small town in Nebraska and the big cancer hospital and the specialists are in New

York City or Houston. Are you going to agree to be uprooted from your family and friends and zipped across the country to be treated for six weeks or three months? Don't forget, we're talking about cancer: people don't want to go into a room filled with cancer patients. This is a very emotional situation.

More and more places are now establishing tumor committees. At our hospital, all cases of cancer, private and ward, are reviewed by the tumor committee. And there's a lot of talent sitting around this table every Friday morning: the radiologist who does the radiotherapy, the chemotherapist, cancer surgeons. There are about ten of us who discuss every single case of cancer that comes in, and we make recommendations to the patient's doctor.

I think this practice is good in many ways. The private doctor who is doing less cancer work than these individuals doesn't lose contact with his patient. The patient after all went to *him*. Yet through the committee, this doctor is gaining expert opinions about what theoretically should be done for his patient. He in turn has an advantage over the experts because he knows a lot about this person that the committee doesn't. At least I hope he does. It's easy to teach medical students how you treat cancer. Cancer of the cervix is treated a, b, c, and d. But it isn't cancer of the cervix we're talking about. We're talking about a *woman* with cancer of the cervix. The tumor committee has all the information about her medical condition, whether she can tolerate the proper operation. But her own doctor may come to us and say, "I *know* this woman. If you go up there and tell her what you're planning, she's going to jump out the window."

I think the problem with many a cancer specialist is he's so damned eager to prove he's the biggest surgeon in the world that he can lose sight of the fact that he's dealing with people. You see, not only does a cancer surgeon have to be aggressive and attack the disease, but he tends to become a cold sort of person. He has to set up some defense. He can't afford to get too close to his patients. They're going to *die* on him, and a little bit of him dies every time they do. So he loses a certain amount of softness and resists a warm doctor-patient relationship if he's doing only cancer. I'm not sure that's good for him or for the patient. Therefore, while I can appreciate the reason for cancer specialty boards on the one hand, I'm not sure that doctors should really do just cancer.

I couldn't. I like to operate, but sometimes I like to just take out a cyst and cure somebody. I don't understand how a nurse can be on a hospital's pediatric ward and every day go in and watch these kids die of cancer. Sweet, beautiful-looking little children. I'd go out of my mind.

24. Doctors and Medicine

How do you pick a doctor?

This is a good basic question people sometimes ask. One way is to choose the man who's got the largest practice. But I think some of the biggest practices are held by the worst doctors.

If you're in a large community, you might think, I'll go to the medical school or hospital and get the head of the department. He should be the best doctor. Baloney. That's not true anymore. A long time ago, the heads of clinical departments at hospitals and medical schools were clinicians, or practicing doctors. But today the heads of clinical departments tend to be researchers who have no relationship to patients. They have no practice and perhaps have never had a practice. The head of Surgery may not be a surgeon. The head of Medicine may be a bacteriologist who's done everything in research and now is running a clinical department.

How did researchers get into these positions?

They got the power to run departments because back when the clinicians were department chiefs, the government said,

"Look, we want to give money to the hospital." But the clinician-heads were reluctant to take the government's money because they were afraid of bureaucrats and afraid the government was going to come in and tell them how to run their practices, their departments or their patients. So they said, "No, we don't want your money, but we have a little guy in the back room in a tattered white coat who's working on tsetse flies or rats—what difference does it make if the government runs his business? He's not working with patients. So if you've got some money, give him some grants."

Well, hospitals, and medical schools particularly, are like whores: they'll go to the guy with the most money. Suddenly the medical schools looked up and there was the guy in the back room with this grant money coming in for his research. Since medical schools take 12½ percent right off the top of everybody's research grant to administrate the grant, the more money that comes in for grants, the more money the medical school will have. And they've got to get money somewhere. Students don't pay their own way by a long shot.

So the little guy in the back room was suddenly in command. The school wanted to keep this research man and his money. Therefore, when they started making new appointments for heads of departments, they put the research people in charge. I think the head of a department, whether it's Surgery or Pediatrics or whatever, should be the best administrator, the best teacher, but most important, the best *doctor*—surgeon or pediatrician—in his specialty. Nobody can be all that, but the head of a clinical department should certainly be a clinician. If people in his department get in trouble, he should be the man who's called to help them out.

Now ironically, the very thing a lot of us doctors fought— Medicaid and Medicare—is probably going to help get the clinician back in power. Look what's happened to the research grant since the start of the Vietnam war: there are no more grants available. What money comes from Washington has been diverted to support the new Medicaid and Medicare laws. Now the clinicians are getting this money for their patients. And that old whore medical school is looking around again. Until we get the clinicians back in charge, though, you can't count on the department head as being the best doctor.

How can you find a good doctor?

One way is to start by asking the County Medical Society for a list of doctors in the specialty you need. You can then take those names to the library, where there are books that list doctors—*The Directory of Medical Specialists* published by Marquis, for example—and you can look up these people to see what their training was. A guy who's been well trained should be a better than average doctor. Probably he's been associated with one of the bigger hospitals, because they get first crack at the best interns. A twenty-bed hospital in the Okefenokee Swamps in Florida can't compete with Massachusetts General Hospital or New York Hospital or the other big hospitals where the teaching is better and the experience broader. If you are going to a specialist, you should also make sure that he is certified by the specialty board in his field. Most people don't realize that any doctor can call himself a specialist in any field, including surgery, even though he has not received specialty training or board certification.

In the long run, the best way to choose a doctor is to find out who takes care of the other doctors' families, or most of the nurses. You can call a hospital and ask for a chief resident in, say, Obstetrics and Gynecology, and then ask him who takes care of the doctors' wives. That's the surest way to find the best man.

Of course, you may not like a doctor as an individual. It's amazing how important the personality of your physician is. But you're not married to him. You can always leave and go somewhere else. At least you'll be able to start out with someone you know is good.

What do you think of consulting opinions?

I think any doctor who's not willing to have another opinion is not worth his salt. I'm not necessarily going to be operated on because one doctor says I need to be. One thing that worries a good surgeon is how many unnecessary operations are being sold. We're not only physicians here to heal people, we're salesmen, too. Since I'm a gynecologist, I'm in the business of selling myself, the hospital I'm sending my patient to and the operation my patient is going to have. Of course you must have confidence in the honesty and ability of your doctor. However, I tell my patients frankly, especially if it's a question of a major operation, "It's very easy for me to sit here and sell you the operation, so if you want another opinion, go get it. I'll be happy to send the records to whomever you choose. The only thing I ask is that you go to somebody good. And if you don't know another doctor, I'll give you some names and you can proceed from there." If a doctor is convinced that you need an operation, why wouldn't he put his decision on the line? Now there are sometimes legitimate differences of opinion, and then the woman has to make a choice. But usually if I've got good indications for surgery, another doctor will agree with me, and nine times out of ten, my patient comes back.

Don't doctors tend to protect each other by agreeing with what a colleague has said?

To a certain extent we protect the profession. I'll go to a party and a lady will say to me, "Oh, I go to Dr. So-and-so. I had four children, all by Dr. So-and-so, is he good?" What am I going to say? "No, you go to a lousy schnook!"? I say, "Yes, he's a good doctor." I don't know about other professions—whether people say, "I just had my divorce with John Jones, is he a good lawyer?" But certainly we're often put in an impossible situation when somebody asks if his doctor is good.

So to that extent we protect our peers. But amongst ourselves, we don't protect anyone. When we have conferences in our specialty—and I go to GYN Conference at the hospital at four o'clock every Monday afternoon—we don't pull any punches if we think somebody did something wrong. By the same token, if a woman comes into my office who I think doesn't need an operation another doctor wants to perform, I give her an honest, frank opinion.

Do some patients shop around hoping to be told what they want to hear?

Yes, and I think that's wrong. If a woman goes to enough doctors, although the first three say, "You need that operation," she'll find one who says, "No, you don't need it," and she'll stick with him.

Usually we can tell the patient who is shopping the minute we see her in the examining room. She's one step ahead of us. I say, "Have you seen another doctor about this?" "No." But she's already in the stirrups, or all set for what comes next. Then we go into my office and I say what I think and *then* she says, "Well, I've been to see Dr. Somebody Else. . . ."

It's hard to fool a doctor. We've seen too many patients and had too much experience. Sometimes a woman comes in faking pain, but it's not hard to find out whether she's malingering. For instance, I'll have her uterus in my examining hands and oh, the lady's in agony. Okay, fine. Then I go to the right side and say, "Does this hurt?"

"No, it doesn't hurt."

I go to the left side: "Does that hurt?"

"Oh yes, that hurts."

Then I go back to the uterus, which hurt first, and I say, "Now you said this doesn't hurt, does it?"

And she says, "No, this doesn't hurt."

And I've got hold of the same uterus I had a minute ago.

Do you think medicine in the U.S. is going to be socialized?

Yes, there's no doubt about it. The private practice of medicine as we know it will no longer exist.

How will socialized medicine work?

Several legislative proposals are currently under consideration. No one knows which one Congress will pass, or in precisely what form. However, there has already been a bill that almost got through the New York State legislature that in essence would have eliminated the private practice of medicine. It gives a general idea of how a national system would work.

According to the New York State bill, groups of doctors would be formed under the auspices of, or at least connected with, a hospital. You, the subscriber, would pay a fixed amount per month to the state licensed insurance company. For that, you would get complete medical care when you needed it. The insurance company, in turn, would pay your hospital and doctors' bills. Depending on the policy of each group, member doctors would receive a salary and/or fee, with some of the insurance company's money being allocated to pay for overhead and equipment.

Suppose, for example, there were a million people in the group, each paying $3 a month. There wouldn't be a million people sick at the same time, so the money coming in would pay for those who were sick. Presumably the administrators would invest any surplus capital in order to accrue more money.

Under this system, when you got sick, you'd go to your medical group and would be treated by whoever was available. If you wanted your own private physician, you could have him, but not within one of these groups. And if he was not affiliated with a group and you needed hospitalization, the insurance company would refuse to pay your hospital bill. How could most people afford this, with the cost of hospitalization as high as it is? You'd be forced to go to the group to be covered in case you had to be hospitalized. In big cities like New York, there will always be some private physicians, because there will always be people who want their personal doctor and can afford to have him—but they'll only be the rich minority. In smaller towns throughout the country, private practice is doomed.

Why would groups be a necessary basis of socialized medicine?

For reasons of economy and efficiency. First of all, the insurance company would deal with a group, as opposed to thousands of individual doctors. These groups, comprising doctors in various specialties, would share facilities—an entire building or several floors of offices. By maximum utilization of equipment and personnel, they would theoretically cut overhead and costs. An X-ray machine would not stand idle. Nursing specialists would work for several doctors. Patients could get the different services they needed within one physical unit. Patients' charts would be centrally filed and sent down the hall or upstairs to the doctor who required them.

Why couldn't a patient have his personal physician within a group? Couldn't each doctor agree to take a certain number of patients on his permanent list?

Theoretically this would be possible if the group was small enough and decided that's how it would run things. But consider the realities of twenty physicians in practice together. Even though they are equally qualified medically, some are going to be more popular with the patients. Are you going to have ten doctors whose schedules are jammed with waiting patients, while ten others have time to spare? I suppose the group could accept the inefficiency of that situation and perhaps pay the busier doctors more. In essence, then, the group would have decided to conduct itself as though its members were in private practice. But this eliminates many of the basic advantages doctors want from group practice: sharing of the work load, more regular hours and more time off. More important, the insurance company could never afford to allow this inequality and inefficiency. There are not enough doctors today to start with, and when socialized medicine becomes available, the number of patients will increase.

We have a couple of working examples of socialized medicine now. The largest is the Kaiser-Permanente group health insurance program on the West Coast, with about 1,500,000 subscribers. Second largest is the Health Insurance Plan (H.I.P.) of Greater New York, with about 740,000 subscribers, more than half of whom are employees of the New York City government. Recently H.I.P. encountered financial and organizational problems, and in an article describing a compromise 15 percent rate increase for subscribers, *The New York Times* said, "The future of the organization has become important nationally because it is the closest example New York has to a health maintenance organization, the prepaid health financing and service plan backed by the Nixon Administration."

Even H.I.P., which works on a limited scale, will not promise a subscriber that he can become the patient of the doctor he chooses. Nor will H.I.P. promise him that, having started seeing one doctor, he will continue to be treated on subsequent visits by the same man. The mere numbers involved are going to make this kind of personal consideration impossible. The Nassau County, Long Island, H.I.P. group, which according to the *Times* "was set up as a model of prepaid medical practice," has more than 60,000 subscribers in two centers.

Realistically speaking, what's happening with H.I.P. groups now is that some of them assign their doctors a panel of patients. If the doctor's panel is not full, a new patient can get on it. Once on, that patient will be scheduled to see "his" doctor if possible. But the patient may turn up and find his appointment has been switched to another man. Where the group is flexible and responsive to individuals, the patient making an appointment can ask whether a particular doctor is off that day, or out operating or having office hours. If this information is divulged, the patient can then try to arrange his visit so the doctor he wants will be there. But many patients who use H.I.P. for certain services go to private doctors —obstetricians, for example—when they feel they want more of a doctor's time and a personal, ongoing relationship. As a matter of fact, H.I.P. has lost more than 30,000 subscribers throughout the state in the last four years.

How do you feel about socialized medicine?

I don't like the prospect at all, although theoretically the system sounds good. I mean, a patient comes to the group and everything is there. She's seen, much as she is in diagnostic clinic, by an internist first. A history and general physical are done, and then the internist summons everybody he needs, in whatever specialty he needs—a gynecologist or an orthopedist or an obstetrician or whatever. The X-rays are all there, all the tests are done, and if everything's going to be free, well, fine, as a doctor I'd rather not have to think about cost. And we do. There are times when I think, "Should I get an X-ray of this? It costs seventy dollars. Can she afford seventy dollars? Well, we won't get the X-ray this time." So theoretically, groups or socialized medicine sound good.

But look at any system that has this. Look at the stateside medicine in the armed forces: certainly not the best medicine in the world. Look at Great Britain, where you can still have your private physician if you can afford him: certainly not the top medical care in the world. I'm egotistical enough to think that in our country, considering the size and mixture of the population, we've got the best available medical care.

They think—"they" being the politicians and the public —that they're going to get better medical care under socialization, but they're going to get worse medical care. They think it's going to be free, but it's not. Nothing in this world is free. Somebody will be paying for it and that somebody will be the taxpayer. Furthermore, socialized medicine will cost more in the long run because the system is wasteful. So I'm depressed about the outlook of medicine, for myself as a physician, for the profession as a whole, and for the public, which is going to suffer most.

Why are you depressed for yourself?

First, because I don't like group practice. After being in private practice in New York City for a long time, I joined a couple of other doctors and tried it for two years. It sounded reasonable. This was a private group, set up so that each doctor could have a weekend off when one of the other men would cover for him. On the night he was off, he could have a few drinks without worrying that he was going to get a call. But I didn't like delivering patients I didn't know. My patients didn't like hearing that their doctor was off the night they went into labor and someone else was going to deliver their baby. So I figured when it stopped being fun to be an obstetrician, it was time to leave the group, and I went back into practice alone.

Then a few years later, you quit obstetrics, didn't you?

Yes. But the decision was based primarily on a choice I had to make between delivering babies or doing a great deal of surgery. I couldn't have continued as an obstetrician even in a group and taken on the numbers and kinds of operations I wanted to do.

I'm not saying there should be no groups. There are many private groups or partnerships in existence now, and I can understand some doctors—obstetricians more than most— wanting that relief. What I object to is a law which penalizes the physician who wants to remain in private practice by making his patients pay their own hospital costs. This has nothing to do with whether I'm an obstetrician. It affects me just as much as a gynecologist. And a patient doesn't have to be pregnant to want an ongoing personal relationship with her physician. When a lady calls me to talk about her mother's mastectomy, I don't think she'd feel so good if the secretary said, "I'm sorry, it's Dr. Sweeney's night off, would you like to talk to Dr. X?" I don't believe most patients realize what it will be like to go to a group, talk to a doctor, often about a personal problem, and next time go back, maybe for the same problem, and get another doctor and have to start all over with him.

What other objections do you have to socialized medicine?

One, of course, is financial. I'll charge a patient, say, $500 for a hysterectomy, and the insurance company will come along and say, "We only pay $350 for a hysterectomy, will you accept that as your total fee?" If I don't, the patient has to pay the difference. This rate setting isn't my chief objection, although it's a strong one. People think doctors are rich, but they aren't. They make a good living—when they get around to it. Still, they've got nine or ten years' postcollege training, while the majority of guys they attended college with went right into jobs. Most doctors start out feeling a little behind in the financial area.

The main reason I don't want socialized medicine, aside from the prospect of group practice, is that it's going to be worse medicine and it's going to be more expensive medicine. Doctors are going to suffer from it, but most important, patients will, too.

Why is it going to be worse medicine?

That's a complex question, and I'm going to give a long answer. Basically, both the doctors and the system itself are going to make it worse medicine.

To begin with, the kids today don't want to work as hard as we did. They want to work from nine to five and then go home. They're interested in the fringe benefits. They want a month's vacation with pay. They want their Blue Cross and Blue Shield paid for. They want annuity plans. They want their kids sent to college. And when everybody's in groups, they're going to get all these benefits and be paid a salary just like anybody else. Why do guys become cops? Not because they want to become cops more than anything else in the world. More likely because of the security, even though the salaries are not that high.

Now, I'm an older doctor and I'm saying, "In the old days, it was better." This is sour grapes, perhaps. Maybe nobody wants to work as hard nowadays. But this attitude is deadly when you're talking about medicine. What kind of care do you think the patient's going to get who hits the clinic at quarter of five when the doctor wants to get out of there at five? If a patient comes in here at quarter to five, we don't leave until we're finished. If it's seven o'clock, everybody's here till seven. But this dedication to patient care is disappearing—or certainly it's deteriorating sharply. I'm not the only one who'll say this by a long shot. Senior doctors in every specialty in all the hospitals are complaining about the quality of their house staff.

I had a lady admitted to the hospital with a great big wine-stain nevus on her face—a birthmark—you've seen them. The whole left side of her face was a nevus. I looked at the intern's workup on her and it said, "Head and neck: negative." Now if he skipped that, which was staring him in the face, what else did he skip? When I see a guy work like that, I'll tell him a thing or two. He'll never miss another one. There's no room in this business for sloppiness, or half-dedication or cutting corners.

I sometimes wonder how these kids think they're going to

learn. They don't want to do any of the menial tasks. They want to operate and deliver babies. But they don't want to do the so-called scut work of drawing bloods, doing routine pelvic exams or keeping records or charts. Well, a doctor spends the rest of his life making records, keeping charts on his patients. I don't like writing up charts, so I type mine, even though I'm only a one-finger typist, because that way I force myself to make them more complete. Otherwise you get tired of writing notes by hand and you find yourself cheating. You put down "As before." "As before!" That's no kind of record.

The interns object to dictating operative notes, so they lose the benefit of reviewing the procedure step by step. Yet that's valuable experience. After a while, you don't have to think about what you should do next. Furthermore, the notes dictated after each operation or examination are important. Too many times our Tumor Clinic finds there's not enough information in a chart to enable us to decide how a patient should be treated. Somebody will ask, "How big was the uterus?" And the chart doesn't say how big the uterus was or what the change has been. Yet we can't get it across to these young doctors that their notes are really important.

Now the first time one of them gets sued will be the last time he doesn't make good charts. He gets on the stand and the lawyer says, "What did you do about the sutures?"

"Well, I took out the sutures on the fifth day."

"Prove it."

No proof. Nothing in the chart. No case. How much do you want, lady? All he needed was an entry saying, "Sutures were taken out on the fifth day and a small defect was noted in the upper portion of the incision; we cleaned it and applied a dry sterile dressing." Fine. That's exactly what happened. Suppose on the eighth day this incision broke down and the patient sued. Well, lots of incisions will open up.

Nobody did anything wrong. But a lawyer could just take the doctor apart for that note he didn't make.

We have a room where the curettages and minor procedures are performed. When I was on the house staff, we scrubbed with the doctor who was going to do the procedure and then went ahead with him and did all those pelvic examinations. Afterward, we dictated the notes about what he had done. Maybe we shouldn't have dictated the notes even for minor procedures if he performed them, but we did get the experience of all those pelvic examinations, even if they were normal. Today, there's no house staff in the minor operations room. I go in there alone. I don't need to do another pelvic exam. I've been doing them for twenty-three years. The interns need it, but they don't see that. They're assigned somewhere else, because they didn't like the idea of examining the patient, who probably had a normal pelvis, then having the doctor perform the operation while they had to write up the chart. So now we write up those charts, too. I don't mind it. As a matter of fact, I'd rather do it myself in a way: I'll get a better note than the intern would give me. However, his attitude is going to make medicine a lot different, no question about it.

You can see this even among the students. I went over to the medical school at eleven one recent morning to give a lecture on cancer of the vulva. There were about thirty students in the class, and after the lecture, I told them, as usual, that they were welcome to come up to the operating floors to see the patients. "But we're not going to call you," I said. "It's up to you. By the way, how many of you saw the Couvelaire uterus the other day?"

One student out of thirty had seen it, although they knew it was a rare thing. Couvelaire is a man's name, and a Couvelaire uterus results when a placenta separates prematurely and shears off inside the uterus while the baby's still in there.

If the whole thing comes off, then the woman bleeds into her uterus. It turns black or blue, and the baby dies. We used to do a hysterectomy for this. It was felt the uterus wouldn't contract or would stop functioning after the bleeding into it. However, this assumption has been proven wrong. Now we do a Caesarean section, sew up the uterus and that woman is okay. But how are these students going to learn if they just can't be bothered to come up to the observation room and look at examples? It's going to take them a long time in practice before another one of these comes along, and if they've never seen one, how are they going to handle it? It's a little late at that point to look in the textbook and find out what you're supposed to do. Anyway, the texts still largely say, "Take the uterus out."

I hate to say this, but frankly, they're not making doctors the way they used to. By and large, the current generation doesn't want to go out into private practice. They want to do family planning, take a job with the Population Council or go full-time with a hospital or join groups. They don't want the responsibility or financial outlay of running an office. Opening an office involves borrowing the money to buy all the equipment and then paying it back to the bank. It costs about $50,000 a year just to maintain my office, which has two examining rooms. I've got to have a secretary; that's $10,000 right there. I have to have a nurse, another $10,000. Then there's the rent, the utilities—our phone bill is tremendous, something you wouldn't believe—the supplies, my answering service. When I went into practice, my malpractice insurance cost me $90; today the same coverage costs me $5,000.

Okay, the next question is, what's the difference whether a doctor has made a financial outlay and gone into private practice, or joined a socialized medicine group? Idealistically speaking, I agree that intrinsic motivation should be the driving force behind anybody's doing his job well. But in a less than utopian world, I think that financial responsibility and personal reputation are strong incentives for a man to be the best whatever-it-is he knows how to be. Look at the quality of service provided by the Welfare Department or any other government-run agency. Not many people continue to strive for excellence or dedicate huge amounts of energy and emotion to work if their efforts are not recognized. Yet much of the public will expect the doctor to be different.

One thing which really worries me is what caliber of medical student we're going to draw in ten or twenty years under socialized medicine. How much attraction is that system going to have for the bright young guy who wants a challenge and a chance to go out and prove himself?

Do you see good features about the new generation of doctors?

Of course. I think many are extremely bright. Some are not only skilled but truly dedicated and have a great sense of humanitarianism.

Are salaries for young doctors better than when you trained?

Yes, salaries have improved, and that's as it should be. To take a resident with several years of experience and expect him to be happy with $1,000 a year because he has come to be trained at the great white tower of medicine is ridiculous. I think it's right that residents today get a living wage— $10,000 or $12,000 a year.

Why did you say that socialized medicine is going to be more expensive medicine?

Because of the wastefulness of the system. What is third-party payment, after all, but a cumbersome bureaucracy that's going to be imposed on top of everything and send your costs skyrocketing? Something like this has happened in hospitals in recent years as a result of the insurance companies. It doesn't really cost $75 to get an X-ray of the chest, but the hospital will charge $75 because the insurance companies will pay that much. It isn't coincidence, when you go down a hospital bill, that the charges and allowances are mostly identical. It says **RBC** (red blood count) Cost: $10. Allowance: $10. The hospital will ask for as much as it can get, and since the insurance company can raise its premiums, it's going to pay more so it can tell its clients they're fully covered. The main problem with third-party payments is that nobody has a real incentive to keep costs down. The money's coming from some anonymous source—which just happens to be you and me.

On top of that, there's the inefficiency of such a system. A good example is what happened with a law passed recently in New York State regarding laboratory work. Formerly, when a patient came to this office and needed blood tests or other work, we would send it to the laboratory. The laboratory would send us the test results, and we would bill the patient for her lab fees. We would have a flat deal with the laboratory: you do all our work and we'll pay you a flat figure. Of course, the sum was roughly in relation to the amount of work we estimated they'd be doing for us, and there was a reasonable profit for the labs built in.

Then the government came along and said you can't do that anymore. The labs are going to bill the patients directly, because that will stop the doctor from making any profit on the lab work. Now most doctors weren't making money on lab work, although I'm sure a few were. Actually, it was hard to say what we should charge the patient, because our cost wasn't just the cost of the lab itself, but of our time in securing the specimen, evaluating the report that came back, filing the results in the patient's chart, informing the patient and so forth. Anyway, the old system was outlawed, and what happened? First of all, the lab fees went up because the labs had to create new billing systems to keep up with a hundred patients a day, where before they'd just billed a few doctors once a month. Who pays for the expensive new billing system? The patient. Next, these labs began having trouble collecting on their bills. They had been paid by the doctor every month and could work their profit on that. But now their collections are somewhere around 40 to 50 percent. A lot of patients afraid of not paying their doctor just don't pay these labs. And the fees involved are so small the lab can't afford to sue the patient. So they write it off. But they can't run a business that way, so they increase their rates to compensate for this 50 percent that's not paying. Now all patients are being charged more as a result of this stupid law than they ever were by the few doctors who were making a profit on lab tests.

That's the kind of thing that's going to happen economically when we socialize medicine. Costs are going to spiral. It's going to take millions and billions of dollars just to pay for the machinery of the thing. And people think they're going to get something for nothing.

Are you satisfied with medicine in the United States today?

No. I don't think any doctor can ever afford to be satisfied. Particularly when it comes to the medical care as well as the living conditions of many poor people in this country, I think there is tremendous need for improvement. But I believe that selective assistance, such as Medicare and Medicaid, more clinics and education in the use of such facilities are better means of insuring the finest medical care in the most economical way.

What has stopped socialized medicine until now?

First, the medical profession itself. Second, the people. People wanted to choose their doctor and have a personal relationship with him. This preference goes back to the beloved general practitioner-family doctor. But recently, especially with more of the population living longer, the politicians have figured out that enough people will want socialized medicine if they think they can have it for free to make it a popular issue. Supporting socialization can buy a lot of votes.

What's going to make socialized medicine pass, finally, is

that the kids in medical school today and the interns and residents want it. The older doctors who have always fought socialization are still against it. But the young doctors now want to try things this way.

I say I'll quit if socialized medicine comes about, but I won't. I'll live with it. Medicine is my life.

INDEX

Abnormal baby: thalidomide, 51; heart defect, 169–170. *See also* Brain damage.

Abortion, 204–213; and guilt, 209–210, 212–213; by manual curette, 205–206; pain after, 211; salting out, 207–208; by suction curette, 206–207

Adoption, 81; influencing conception, 105

Afterbirth. *See* Placenta.

Alzheimer's disease, 127

Amniotic fluid, 56, 159. *See also* Membranes.

Analgesic, 269–270. *See also* Demerol; Scopolamine.

Anesthesia: obstetrical, 269–273; surgical, 187, 189. *See also* Analgesic; Caudal block; Epidural block; Gas; Novocaine; Paracervical block; Pentothal; Pudendal block.

Apgar, 235

Artificial insemination. *See* Infertility.

Atropine, 163

Baby: appearance of newborn, 60, 64; appearance of postmature (late), 175; care of newborn, 166; care of newborn in distress, 60–64; mother jealous of, 134–135. *See also* Premature baby.

Birth. *See* Childbirth.

Birth control methods, 251–258; prescribing for young girls, 78. *See also* Birth control pills; Coitus interruptus; Condom; Creams and jellies; Diaphragm; Douche; IUD; Rhythm method; Suppositories; Tubal ligation; Vaginal foams; Vasectomy.

Birth control pills, 251–254; blood clots and, 252; cancer and, 252; dosage, 251–252; effectiveness, 254; forgetting to take, 18–19; safety of, 251–252; side effects, 253–254; women who should not take, 253; working of, 251

Bleeding: abnormal and postmenopausal, 119–120; between periods, 77–78; "breakthrough bleeding," 253; during menopause, 118–119; during pregnancy, 147, 220–229; spotting mid-cycle, 244. *See also* Bloody discharge; Hemorrhage; Menstrual period; Ovary.

Bloody discharge: after delivery (lochia), 44; before labor (show), 158

Blues: postpartum, 133–135. *See also* Depression.

Brain damage (in infant), 61–62

Breast cancer, 42–43, 282. *See also* Mastectomy.

Breast examination by patient, 282
Breast lump, 42, 282
Breast-feeding, 173

Caesarean section, 163–168; no limit to number of, 163; option, 229; reasons against, 92–93, 228; reasons for, 58, 91–93, 161–163, 226
Cancer, 124–126, 280–291; allowing patient to die, 286–287; appearance of patient with advanced, 215; and birth control pills, 252; of breast (*see* Breast cancer); of cervix (*see* Cervical cancer); definition of, 126; fear of, 280; and hormones, 124–126, 252–253; inoperable, 79, 214; as medical specialty, 289–291; of ovary (*see* Ovarian cancer); predicting outcome, 280–281; telling patient she has, 287–289; treatment, 192, 282–287; of uterus (*see* Uterine cancer); of vagina (*see* Vaginal cancer)
Caput, 54–55
Castration, 181–182
Catheter (to empty bladder), 279
Caudal block, 272–273
Centimeter, 26–27, 54
Cervical cancer, 214–218, 283–284; detection (by Pap smear), 281–282
Cervix: appearance of, 20; dilation during labor, 26–27, 53–54. *Illus.*, 240
Change of life. *See* Menopause.
Childbirth, 35–39, *Illus.*, 241. *See also* Delivery; Labor.
Coitus interruptus, 255–256
Colostomy, 283–284
Conception, 243–244; difficulty with (*see* Infertility)

Conceptus, 24
Condom, 256
Consulting opinions, 295–296
Contraception. *See* Birth control methods.
Contractions. *See* Labor.
Cord. *See* Umbilical cord.
Couvelaire uterus, 305–306
Cramps (menstrual), 244-246
Creams and jellies (contraceptive): 255; use with diaphragm, 254

Death: defining, 287; and ending terminal support, 286–287; of infant, 61–62 (*see also* Abnormal baby)
Delivery: doctor missing, 154–155; and holding baby back, 155; low-forceps, 176–179; mid-forceps, 57–60; mother's hands strapped during, 31–32, 58; position of mother during, 274–275; of premature baby, 228–231. *See also* Birth; Caesarean section.
Delivery room; transfer from labor room to, 54–55, 175–176
Demerol, 48, 170–171, 269–270
Depression: during menopause, 120–121; postpartum, 133–135; pre-menstrual, 247–248
Diaphragm, 254
D and C (dilatation and curettage), 78, 209; as abortion method, 205; for cancer diagnosis, 119–120
Dilation of cervix during labor, 26–27, 53–54
Discharge. *See* Bloody discharge; Vaginal discharge.
Diuretic, 247
Doctor: selecting, 292–294; protecting colleagues, 295–296

316 *Index*

Labor (*cont.*)
134, 152–153; infusion during, 33–34; long, 171; pain relief during (*see* Analgesic; Anesthesia); progress of, 47–56; short, 167–168; start of, 153, 158–160; vaginal examination during, 26, 226, 229
Laparotomy, 23
Lochia, 44
Lordotic position, 151

Mammogram, 42
Marijuana: effect on offspring, 149; and sexual pleasure, 261–262
Mastectomy, 42–43, 67–68
Meconium, 56
Membranes (rupture of): spontaneous, 154, 159–160; reasons for, 56, 162, 229
Menopausal symptoms: hot flushes, 117–118; other, 120–121; estrogen deficiency as cause of, 121; Premarin to alleviate, 118–119
Menopause, 116–128; and bleeding, 118–120; and changes in breasts, 123–124; and changes in clitoris, 124; and changes in facial hair and features, 123–124; and changes in hair and skin, 121; and changes in uterus, 123–124; and changes in vagina, 122–123; and changes in voice, 123–124; fear of, 126–128; and hormones, 124–128, 253; onset of, 117, 119, 127; and sex drive, 121–122. *See also* Menopausal symptoms.
Menstrual period, 243–248; blood loss during, 245; and breast changes, 247; and complexion

problems, 247; and cramps, 244–246; and depression, 247–248; and fatigue, 245; and headaches, 247; infrequent, 78; and monthly cycle, 243–244; and poor sleep, 247–248; and psychological factors, 247–248; scanty, 254; and water retention, 247. *See also* Bleeding.
Miscarriage, 23–25; care of woman with history of, 220–229
Morphine, 269–270

Natural childbirth, 27, 32–33, 48–51, 167–168
Novocaine, 59, 273

Omentum, 190
Oophorectomy, 181–183; 186–193; reasons for, 78–80, 182–183; fear of, 181–182
Ovarian cancer, 78–80; 189–193; symptoms of, 282
Ovary: appearance, 188; bleeding from, 23; cancer of (*see* Ovarian cancer); conception with one, 244; cyst on, 278; function of, 243–244; removal of (*see* Oophorectomy). *Illus.*, 240
Ovulation: temperature chart to determine, 78, 103–104. *See also* Reproductive cycle.
Oxygen: for laboring mother, 56–57; for newborn infant, 61–64; supply to fetus, 60

P-32 tubes, 191–192
Pap smear, 72–73, 281–282
Paracervical block, 53–54, 59, 270–271
Pathology Lab, 24, 189–193
Pelvic infection. *See* Gonorrhea; Syphilis